Department of The Environment

Development of Evaluative Framework and
Review of Existing Spoil Disposal Procedures

Mineral Planning Research Project PECD 7/1/118–180/83

Assessment of Alternative Colliery Spoil Disposal Options

Produced for the Department by Ove Arup & Partners

London   Her Majesty's Stationery Office

© Crown copyright 1988
First published 1988
ISBN 0 11 752122 1

D
622.33
DEV

CONTENTS

CONTENTS - cont'd

EXECUTIVE SUMMARY

A. Background to the Project

Spoil is the waste material that is extracted by the National Coal Board (now renamed British Coal) in the process of mining deep coal. A limited amount is left either underground or in saleable coal, or is sold commercially, but this still currently leaves around 50 million tonnes to be disposed of nationally each year. About two-thirds of this volume is tipped in the Yorkshire, Nottinghamshire, Derbyshire coalfield where problems in finding sufficient tipping capacity are becoming more difficult.

Concern about the environmental impacts of spoil disposal was one of the major issues raised by the Commission on Energy and the Environment which reported in 1981. Similar concerns were also raised at two major Public Inquiries (Vale of Belvoir and South Kirkby) at about the same time. Part of the Government's response to these concerns, given in the White Paper of May 1983 "Coal and the Environment", was to set up this Research Project. A smaller Public Inquiry into a tip extension has since taken place in South Wales.

The main aim of the Project was to design and construct an Evaluative Framework to assist decision making on the selection of options for colliery spoil disposal. A Framework was to be drafted in the early stages of the Project and then tested and successively refined by the examination of a series of case studies. These case studies had been selected to reflect a variety of disposal arrangements and to take account of different financial and environmental considerations. A description of the purpose and development of the Evaluative Framework is presented in the Final Report. The Framework itself is presented in a self contained Procedural Manual guiding its use. A summary guide describes the essence of the Framework, why it is needed and who should use it.

A. cont'd

A second strand of the Project was to review current spoil disposal procedures. These vary for different types of spoil (coarse and fines discard), by handling method and by location. A four part review has been completed covering Technical, Institutional, Financial and Environmental aspects and the results are summarised in the Final Report.

B. <u>Purpose and Development of the Evaluative Framework</u>

The Evaluative Framework has been developed to improve existing decision making processes with regard to the planning of colliery spoil disposal. It is designed to assist decision making in two main situations:

- during local planning in response to the disposal needs of a particular colliery, and

- to identify appropriate sources of spoil for large scale reclamation projects.

For most effective use it relies on close working relationships between the National Coal Board (NCB) at Area level and the Mineral Planning Authority (MPA).

The two starting points for the design of the Framework were:

- an understanding of the planning context within which it would be used, and

- an examination of existing economic and environmental appraisal techniques.

The nearest equivalent to the type of Framework suitable for assessing disposal options for colliery spoil was considered to be the Department of Transport's framework for trunk road appraisal. This consists of the COBA computer program which uses social cost-benefit appraisal techniques, and the Manual of Environmental Appraisal procedure which summarises impacts by the relevant environmental factors.

B.   cont'd

It was decided that the colliery spoil Framework should be constructed in a similar way to include two separate appraisals proceeding in parallel. However, it was felt desirable to extend the appraisals to include a combined evaluation, to assist the trade off between financial costs and environmental effects in the search for a preferred disposal option.

A three part Evaluative Framework was therefore designed as follows:

Phase I	Selection of Options
Phase II	Cost and Impacts
	– Economic
	– Environmental
Phase III	Combined Evaluation

Phase I provides a checklist procedure for identifying the most realistic options for the disposal of spoil from a particular colliery or group of collieries. The Phase II economic analysis uses financial appraisal techniques and reflects NCB's costing considerations. The Phase II environmental analysis is based on a factor by factor assessment of impact and reflects the wider effects of a scheme on the community. Phase III includes two decision aiding tools (Option Rankings and Pairwise Comparison) intended to assist the selection process.

A draft Evaluative Framework was published as part of the Consultants' Interim Report in 1984. It was then tested and revised sequentially against a series of twelve case study schemes. The early case studies were generally used to test the structure and content of the questionnaires to be used in Phases I and II of the Framework and its general understandability. The later case studies focussed more on the testing of options and in particular the usefulness of the decision aiding techniques.

B.   cont'd

The basic design of a three part process remained firmly intact throughout the testing programme. A certain amount of restructuring was found to be necessary particularly in the environmental analysis, where a two-stage process was consolidated into one and greater emphasis was given to summarising the option differences. Minor amendments were also made to the indicators used to summarise costs in the economic analysis. During the case study programme a computer routine was developed and tested to take the tedium out of the financial calculations.

The decision aiding tools specified in Phase III were found to be useful in different ways. The Option Rankings is a simple, quick technique which can be presented graphically. Pairwise Comparison is a useful way of breaking down a complex problem and eliminating less desirable options in those situations where there are a large number under consideration. A third technique, a Weighting/ Scoring system, was tested during the case study programme. It attracted criticism due to the probable difficulties of different parties agreeing on the relative importance to be placed on costs as against environmental considerations. It was also felt that a technique which produced seemingly simple figure work could easily be open to misinterpretation. It was therefore excluded from the final version of the Evaluative Framework.

C.   Review of Existing Procedures

- Technical

Land-based tipping accounts for over 90% of total annual spoil disposed nationally. Most of this is tipped on spoil heaps although a small amount is used in local land reclamation projects - for example, filling mineral working voids or raising the level of badly drained poor quality land. Marine disposal is restricted to North East England and accounts for about 9% of the spoil disposed.

C.   cont'd

The construction of coarse discard tips is a relatively straight-forward mechanical handling operation. Fines discard is a more difficult substance to handle; it can either be pumped to settling lagoons or it can (at extra cost) be mechanically dewatered and then disposed of on the same tip as coarse discard.

Most land-based tipping is carried out adjacent to collieries although some spoil is taken off-site to backfill mineral voids. Colliery spoil can also be used as a cover material for solid waste landfill sites. However, transport costs remain a deterrent to the more widespread adoption of off-site uses.

Restoration practices adopted for individual schemes are determined by the type of after-use to be achieved. This usually involves return to agriculture or open space. Progressive restoration is now favoured as it ensures the minimum amount of productive land being out of use at any one time. It is however, more difficult to achieve when tailings lagoons are incorporated within the coarse discard tip.

- Institutional

The NCB does not have within its management structure a functional responsibility exclusively devoted to the disposal of colliery spoil. The various officials concerned with spoil disposal are brought together through a series of national and area committees. Officials at Area level are most involved in planning, acquiring and disposing of tipping sites. Although the Colliery Manager has responsibility for overseeing tipping activity during the operational stage, activity is co-ordinated at Area level through the Area Tips Committee. Overall advice on tipping policy and research is provided by HQ.

C.   cont'd

The NCB must apply for planning permission to the relevant MPA for all new colliery spoil disposal schemes. Before formally submitting an application NCB Areas will usually have carried out consultations with the MPA and other parties such as the Ministry of Agriculture, Fisheries and Food (MAFF) and the Nature Conservancy Council, and have completed an environmental checklist. No information is currently submitted to the MPA (nor requested) on the financial aspects of a proposed scheme nor on the results of comparing alternative disposal locations. The use of the Evaluative Framework as developed in this Research Project is designed to make the examination of such information much more explicit.

The majority of formal tipping applications determined by MPAs are approved. Conditions attached to safeguard the surrounding environment are however becoming more stringent. Only two spoil disposal applications have so far gone to Public Inquiry (South Kirkby and Wernos).

Some tipping still takes place as permitted development under the General Development Order, in which case no conditions have been attached. However, the NCB has been prepared to surrender most of these rights when putting forward proposals for new tipping on adjacent land but problems still remain on some sites.

The abolition of the Metropolitan Counties and the transferal of their powers to the geographically smaller District Authorities will increase the possibility of preferred tipping sites for a given colliery being outside that District's area. This situation could give rise to conflict of interests between adjacent authorities. There is, therefore, some level of concern that the strategic planning over-view could become diluted.

C.   cont'd

- <u>Financial</u>

The most comprehensive cost guide for different types of disposal schemes comes from an internal NCB report produced in 1983-84. Although based on actual costs assembled at Area level, they provide the basis for making projections of the differences between disposal locations.

The resulting costs can be summarised as follows:

<u>SPOIL DISPOSAL AS A PROPORTION OF COAL MINING COSTS</u>

Spoil Disposal Location	Cost/Tonne Spoil	Cost/Tonne of Saleable Output	% of Average cost at £37.70/Tonne
	£	£	%
On-site	1.5 - 2.5	0.9 - 1.6	2.4 - 4.2*
Local Off-site	3.1 - 3.4	1.9 - 2.1	5.0 - 5.6*
Remote	6.0 - 10.0	3.8 - 6.2	10.1 - 16.4

Note* These orders of costs are already incurred and reflected in the price of coal.

The range given for each option reflects, at the lower end, the use of lagoons for the disposal of the fines discard element and, at the upper end, the use of dewatering equipment. Transport costs account for the largest element in the composition of local off-site and remote options.

C.   cont'd

Cost estimates produced by the Consultants from the case studies programme were generally lower than the above NCB estimates for each category of option. This is only partly explained by the difference in the cost indicator used. The Consultants' Equivalent Annual Cost measure, based on discounted cash flow techniques, would be expected to give slightly lower figures than the annual operating cost method which includes capital costs by way of allowances for depreciation and interest charges.

There is no evidence to suggest that parties other than the NCB are incurring any substantial direct costs as a consequence of the spoil disposal process. This is in keeping therefore with the spirit of the "Polluter Pays Principle" advocated by the present Government. Although the NCB will accept marginally increased costs to achieve environmental gain for a particular scheme, the site chosen is likely to represent the nearest to a given colliery and hence the least-cost option. The scope for achieving wider use of off-site voids for spoil disposal thus rests on the extent to which some form of cost redistribution is possible.

There is a long list of potential parties who might be expected to contribute by way of subsidy, although each party will have limitations on available cash. It would be appropriate for the NCB to receive some contribution to additional costs:

-   where it is encouraged to adopt a solution which is more expensive than another alternative acceptable on environmental grounds, or
-   where significant enhancements in environmental standards are imposed.

C.   cont'd

- <u>Environmental</u>

There are no easy ways of measuring the environmental effects of spoil disposal schemes because the assessment is largely subjective and because environmental consciousness changes over time. Environmental effects will vary with the:

-    form of disposal (surface tipping, lagooning, backfilling of voids, marine disposal), and

-    type of surroundings (existing colliery/mineral site or farmland, landscape quality, proximity to settlements, presence of any special features).

The impacts will vary over the life of a scheme, particularly between operational and after-use stages. Impacts are also likely to be perceived differently by different interest groups. Nevertheless the environmental effects can be grouped into five main categories:

- visual
- land use
- ecological/heritage/recreational
- pollutants
- transport route.

Of these the first two are virtually certain to occur with any scheme, although there are ways of ameliorating visual impacts. The third category will only occur when special features exist in the locality. The fourth should only represent a risk of pollution rather than a positive impact, and the final category will only occur if the disposal site is located away from the originating colliery.

D.   cont'd

The NCB sees itself as adopting a responsible attitude to the
environment by the maintenance of good working practices. Apart
from this self regulation, the NCB is also encouraged to maintain
environmental standards by the imposition and enforcement of
planning conditions attached to the grant of planning permissions.
Formally updating standards by this means is difficult to introduce
although powers to review permissions are being introduced through
the Minerals Act 1981. Indirect means of setting and updating
standards include existing liaison arrangements between the NCB
and MPAs, feedback from previous permissions, Public Inquiries, and
innovative schemes such as those grant aided by the Department of
the Environment's spoil disposal demonstration fund.

It is not felt appropriate to consider bringing NCB spoil disposal
sites under the Control of Pollution Act 1974 powers because of the
degree of overlap with existing planning conditions and their
ineffectiveness in dealing with restoration issues.

D.   Conclusions

The Evaluative Framework has been carefully designed to improve
existing decision making processes with regard to the disposal of
colliery spoil. It has been tested against a variety of schemes
selected as case studies. It has been shown in testing to be:

- comprehensive
- flexible
- understandable
- clear.

It will obviously need monitoring and further refinement as it is
used in practice.

D.   cont'd

The Evaluative Framework should encourage a more co-ordinated approach to the spoil disposal problem. It is likely to be used most effectively where there are established liaison arrangements between the NCB and MPA. Joint exercises to estimate likely spoil arisings and to establish the various time horizons when new tipping arrangements will be required, will often be a fore-runner to the use of the Framework.

Used in this way it is hoped that the Framework will result in earlier agreement between the NCB and MPA and thus shorten the timescale for granting planning consent. In the event that agreement cannot be reached and a Public Inquiry results, the Framework should at least identify the areas of disagreement from those of agreed fact and provide a structured basis on which investigations can proceed.

Although the scale of spoil production is likely to remain constant nationally over the coming years, it is becoming increasingly concentrated in areas such as the Yorkshire, Nottinghamshire, Derbyshire coalfield as mining capacity contracts in the older coalfields. It will also arise in areas not currently affected by mining, such as the Vale of Belvoir and South Warwickshire as new coalfields are opened up to replace exhausted reserves elsewhere. It does not appear to be a realistic proposition to assume that significantly more colliery spoil can be sold commercially.

New sites for spoil disposal will have to be found and a pre-requisite for tackling the problem on a comprehensive basis is for MPAs to have an understanding of likely spoil arisings in a given area.

D.   cont'd

The NCB has considerably improved its internal procedures regarding spoil disposal over the last few years. The nature of liaison arrangements with MPAs varies considerably however. The NCB is conscious of the need to demonstrate its awareness of the environmental consequences of tipping but more could be done.

The most appropriate method of fines discard disposal remains controversial. The NCB is cautious of mechanical dewatering equipment due to its higher costs and manpower requirements and questionnable reliability. The MPAs prefer the use of dewatering equipment because of the greater chances of achieving progressive restoration when the material is handled dry.

The 1985 Coal Industry Act set NCB a two year target by which to financially break even and a target of 1990 by which to achieve a major degree of self financing. Understandably, therefore, the NCB has to ensure that it is using cost effective disposal methods which, in most cases, means tipping as close to a colliery as possible providing that this is environmentally acceptable. This results in farmland close to collieries being used for tipping when unrestored voids remain available elsewhere.

Although there are other parties who would benefit from the wider use of spoil for reclamation purposes, there is no easily defined formula to produce acceptable cost-sharing. There is an argument to suggest that Central Government should be prepared to assist with the organisation and costs involved in large scale remote disposal schemes, with MPAs or groups of local authorities taking the lead in identifying more local off-site reclamation opportunities.

E.   Recommendations
      ─────────────

A full list of recommendations is included in Chapter 18. The
major ones are:-

-     NCB Areas and MPAs should together use the output of this
      Research Project, the Evaluative Framework, to assist decision
      making on colliery spoil disposal schemes.

-     To assist the understanding and, hence, implementation of the
      Evaluative Framework the DoE should organise a series of
      introductory seminars at regional level, at which the
      Consultants would explain the concept and its details of
      operation.

-     Thereafter the Framework should be monitored and further
      refined as it is used in practice.

To support the practical implementation of the Evaluative Framework
and to improve colliery spoil disposal procedures:

-     The DoE should encourage the implementation of disposal
      schemes which make a significant contribution towards
      reclaiming large scale dereliction and avoiding pressure on
      agricultural land, and should seek a budget accordingly.

-     The DoE should consider extending its current spoil disposal
      demonstration fund to allow the realisation of semi-remote
      disposal schemes, where other parties are prepared to make
      some contribution towards the costs.

-     NCB Areas and MPAs should consider adding to their existing
      liaison arrangements by the establishment of formal Working
      Parties at Area level. This would encourage greater
      co-ordination by allowing the different MPAs covered by an
      Area to be represented (increasingly important after the
      abolition of the Metropolitan County Councils) together with
      other interested parties such as MAFF and the Water
      Authorities.

E.   cont'd

-    NCB Areas should provide regular estimates of spoil production
     to the relevant Mineral Planning Authority to assist the
     forward programming of tipping capacity. An indication of
     land requirements should be capable of being incorporated into
     Structure and Local Plans where appropriate.

-    NCB HQ should consider operating an award scheme to publicise
     best practice in spoil disposal between Areas. Such a scheme
     could be judged by an independent panel of experts in a
     similar way to the Business and Industry Panel for the Envir-
     onment Awards.

The views contained in the Final Report are those of the Consultants and
not necessarily those of the Department of the Environment.

INTRODUCTION

Background to the Project

Between 1979 and 1981 a major investigation on Coal and the Environment was conducted by the Commission on Energy and the Environment (CENE). The Commission concluded that spoil disposal was one of the two most important environmental impacts of deep mining, the other being subsidence. It emphasised that the problem of spoil disposal was as much due to "the lack of any coherent rational or regional disposal policy and indeed from the lack of any machinery for developing a policy" as to the scale of spoil requiring disposal over the next 20 years (Ref.1).

At about the same time as the CENE investigations were taking place, spoil disposal issues were under examination at two Public Inquiries. The first in 1979-80 centred on the proposed development of three new National Coal Board (now renamed British Coal) mines in the North East Leicestershire Prospect (Vale of Belvoir). One of the main concerns raised at the Inquiry and the reason for subsequent refusal was the expected impact of local tipping, particularly at two of the suggested locations. At the time of the planning applications, consideration had not been given to options other than on-site tipping. Similar circumstances surrounded the South Kirkby Public Inquiry in 1981 which was the first Inquiry called specifically to deal with spoil disposal objections.

The Government's response to these mounting concerns was given in May 1983 in the White Paper "Coal and the Environment" (Ref.2). This stated that it had "initiated a major exercise in the Yorkshire, Nottinghamshire and Derbyshire coalfield on spoil disposal, designed to evaluate the main options and to establish a new framework within which spoil decisions can be taken". The Ove Arup & Partners project, commissioned by the Department of the Environment (DoE) in December 1983, forms part of that exercise.

The Project

The project involved three main tasks:-

Task A   -   A review of current spoil disposal methods for different
               types of spoil;

Task B   -   The design and construction of a draft Evaluative
               Framework;

Task C   -   The testing and refinement of the Framework by the exam-
               ination of specified disposal schemes.

The Terms of Reference for the project are reproduced at Appendix A.

The work commenced in December 1983 and lasted over two years. This was
slightly longer than originally intended due to industrial action within
the coal industry in 1984/85 which disrupted field work. The study was
conducted throughout in close consultation with the client Planning and
Steering Groups. The Planning Group comprised representatives of the
DoE, Department of Energy (DEn), NCB HQ and MPAs and met about every
four months. The Steering Group was a larger body including, in
addition to the above representatives, DoE Regional Offices, the
Ministry of Agriculture, Fisheries and Food (MAFF), NCB Areas, Opencast
Executive and County and District Council Associations. It met three
times during the Project.

An Interim Report, covering Tasks A and B, was produced in April 1984.
Following this presentation the primary focus turned to a programme of
12 case studies designed to test the Evaluative Framework. In addition,
research was conducted on two issues which emerged from the Interim
Report namely the respective merits and demerits of alternative means of
disposal for the fines element within colliery spoil; and a comparison
of the problems experienced in the disposal of three other waste
products with similarities to spoil (solid waste, pulverised fuel ash
(pfa) and china clay waste). A thorough assessment was also made of one
of the fundamental issues lying behind this project, namely the extent
to which there is any scope for the redistribution of costs between the
various parties concerned with spoil disposal.

The Final Report

This report marks the culmination of the project. It is designed to be self-contained but draws upon the working papers and case study reports produced during the project. It records the purpose and development of the Evaluative Framework and describes and comments on existing spoil disposal procedures. The Framework itself, together with guidance notes on its use, can be found in the Procedural Manual which accompanies the Final Report. The DoE is shortly expected to commend the use of the Framework to the NCB and Mineral Planning Authorities (MPAs) by means of a DoE Circular.

Although the focus of attention for this project has been the Yorkshire, Nottinghamshire, Derbyshire (Yorks, Notts, Derby) coalfield, this report attempts to provide a national overview to spoil disposal practice. The Evaluative Framework has been designed for use nationally.

The methods of research used in the project have included:-

- literature searches in a number of subject areas;

- a background programme of visits to NCB Areas and planning authorities in the Yorks, Notts, Derby coalfield (and South Wales);

- field work and discussions specifically related to each case study scheme;

- discussions with other Government departments and other interest groups concerned with spoil disposal problems;

- research on other industries with similar waste disposal problems.

The Final Report is in three main parts. The first part charts the steps taken in the development of the Evaluative Framework from its original design, through testing and amendment, to its final design. This part concludes with an appraisal of the final Framework in terms of how well it has fulfilled its original objectives and how it might be used in practice.

The second part describes existing spoil disposal procedures under four main headings:-

- technical
- institutional
- financial
- environmental

It provides reference material describing the context within which the Evaluative Framework was designed.

The third part gives the Consultants' conclusions on the Evaluative Framework and on the main issues facing the NCB and MPAs on existing spoil disposal procedures. These are followed by recommendations for future action.

This report has been produced by Ove Arup & Partners for the DoE. Any views contained in it are those of the authors and not necessarily those of the DoE.

Part 1
Purpose & Development of the Evaluative Framework

1.0 DEVELOPMENT OF THE FRAMEWORK

1.1 Introduction

The main aim of the Project was to design and construct an Evaluative Framework to assist decision making on selecting options for colliery spoil disposal. A Framework was to be drafted in the early stages of the Project, concurrently with the review of existing spoil disposal procedures, and then tested and successively refined by the examination of a series of case studies. The chosen schemes were selected to reflect a variety of disposal arrangements and financial and environmental considerations. The following chapters chart the evolution of the Evaluative Framework from original design, through testing and revision, to the final version.

The two main starting points for the development of the Framework were:-

- an understanding of the planning context within which the Framework would be used and of the procedures currently in use;

- an examination of existing economic and environmental appraisal techniques.

1.2 Existing Planning Context

The NCB must apply for planning permission to the relevant MPA for all new colliery spoil disposal schemes as explained in the Institutional Review in Part 2. However, during the 1970s there was a growing realisation amongst MPAs that the easy options for tipping, particularly on farmland adjoining collieries, were beginning to run out. These problems were especially acute in the Yorks, Notts, Derby coalfield where a large proportion of Britain's mining capacity is now concentrated. The emergence of centralised Coal Preparation Plants fed by several collieries linked underground also increased the need for spoil disposal capacity at certain locations.

1.2 cont'd

There was a danger that a series of incremental extensions could cause environmental problems in some parts of the central coal-field. Yet there was reluctance on the part of the NCB, when submitting a planning application, to consider alternatives to local tipping except in exceptional circumstances. Concern over spoil disposal was one of the key issues raised at the Vale of Belvoir Public Inquiry (1979/80). The South Kirkby Inquiry (1981) was the first to be called entirely on spoil grounds. CENE, reporting in 1981, also drew attention to the lack of any coherent spoil disposal policy. Since then there has been a second Public Inquiry on a tip extension in South Wales. The development of the Evaluative Framework was in part, therefore, a reaction to these concerns.

Since the CENE report, NCB's procedures have been amended inter-nally such that NCB Areas are now advised to complete an environ-mental checklist (see Appendix B) before submitting a planning application in order to check that the disposal scheme has been carefully designed to minimise environmental impact. Extracts from this procedure may sometimes be submitted to the MPA as part of a reasoned justification in support of the application. No infor-mation is currently submitted to the MPA, nor requested, on the financial aspects of a proposed scheme. Nor are alternative locations usually tested although these may have been discussed at officer level by the two parties at informal liaison meetings prior to the submission of the application.

Environmental statements of an increasingly detailed nature have been provided by the NCB before and during recent Public Inquiries into new mine proposals (Park, Selby and Belvoir) and are now being provided for South Warwickshire. Joint appraisal work with the relevant Local Authorities has also taken place in these cases. Sieve mapping techniques were used for the first time by the NCB in the Vale of Belvoir feasibility reports, to take account of envir-onmental factors in the selection of new mine sites (Ref. 3).

1.2 cont'd

There is, as yet, no legal requirement to conduct full Environmental Impact Assessments (EIAs) on any projects in the U.K. However, the EEC Commission over the last few years has been co-ordinating moves towards formalising the EIA approach for major projects. Installations for the disposal of industrial and domestic waste (including colliery spoil) are specified in Annexe 2 of the Directive adopted in June 1985 for application in March 1988, meaning that EIAs may be required at the discretion of an individual member nation.

The construction of the Evaluative Framework has, therefore, taken place at a time when all major developers are having to pay increasing attention to the environmental effects that they create.

The Framework is aimed to assist decision making in two main situations:

- during local planning in response to the disposal needs of a particular colliery, and

- to identify appropriate sources of spoil for large scale reclamation projects.

1.3 Existing Appraisal Techniques

A large variety of techniques exist in the separate fields of economic appraisal and environmental impact assessment. There are few examples however of attempts to provide a technique which combines both aspects. Available techniques, particularly in the environmental field, are often geared more towards the detailed examination and justification of a particular scheme (known as an Environmental Impact Statement) than to the testing and evaluation of more than one option.

1.3 cont'd

Economic Appraisal

There are two main types of economic analyses (financial appraisal and cost benefit analysis) which illustrate the range of possible methods in this field.

Financial appraisal of investment projects involves firstly, the estimation of the expenditure and revenues which accrue to a project for each year of operation and, secondly, the discounting of the cash flows at an agreed discount rate to a common base date. This results in a Net Present Value (discounted revenues minus discounted expenditure) or NPV. The techniques involved are well established and, in commercial terms, are widely accepted as providing an appropriate means to make investment decisions. The advantages of this financial appraisal technique are that the cash flows are directly estimated on actual costs, such as wage rates, market values for materials supply, contract tenders and land purchase, and are assigned to the year in which the cashflow will actually occur.

A disadvantage of the type of financial appraisal technique described above is that the cashflows may omit or inadequately represent the true costs or benefits. There are many areas in which market prices do not or cannot provide adequate measures of the costs or benefits involved. Examples are public health and education provision and road transport infrastructure.

The second method, cost-benefit analysis, attempts to take account of these factors. In such cases, monetary values are placed on the benefits to users arising from the investment and these are set against the costs to the community in a manner similar to the financial investment appraisal.

1.3   cont'd

Two factors can be introduced into cost-benefit analysis as a way of trying to reflect the true costs to the country as a whole rather than just the costs to the developer. These are:-

-   shadow pricing, as a way of reflecting the effect of market distortions such as subsidies, taxation or monopoly pricing;

-   externalities, reflecting the unpaid for consequences of an economic activity such as a pollution impact.

Environmental Appraisal

Environmental appraisal techniques encompass a wide range of methods from the detailed assessment of specific impacts, through a wider treatment of issues such as overlay/sieve methodologies and checklist, matrix or network procedures, to structured environmental statements. Full Environmental Impact Assessments have not been extensively used in the U.K.

The concept of Environmental Impact Assessment originated in the United States in the 1960s and was institutionalised in the National Environmental Policy Act 1970 which required a statement to be prepared of the expected environmental effects for major projects. As conceived, an EIA is concerned with the predictable effects of a project on the environment and therefore involves the identification, quantification and forecasting of each environmental topic.

Because of the long and detailed experience in the U.K. with planning control there has, so far, been no legal requirement to conduct EIAs for any projects. Instead, there has been a tendency to undertake informal EIAs voluntarily, in support of environmentally sensitive planning applications such as petro-chemical developments and water supply issues. Detailed environmental

1.3 cont'd

appraisals have also been made for projects undergoing the rigours of a Public Inquiry; for example major airport developments or nuclear facilities and new coalfields, although they were not necessarily written up as EIAs. Sometimes, the production of such studies has involved joint working between a developer and a local authority.

A detailed review of EIA techniques was produced in 1976 for the Department of the Environment (by Aberdeen University) (Ref. 4). This did not consider that a standard format was necessary, nor that complete quantification of effects was possible. It tended to favour the matrix method for the identification and tabulation of impacts.

Combined Evaluation

Various methods for combining economic and environmental results have been used in the past. In the early 1970s the Roskill Commission into the siting of the Third London Airport converted all the environmental factors into money values to allow the final recommendation to be made solely on economic indicators. This method introduced endless scope for argument and was eventually dismissed when the Government of the day followed Professor Buchanan's minority recommendation which ascribed higher subjective values to the environmental factors than had been included in the monetary analysis.

An alternative method, which removes the necessity of separately weighting economic and environmental factors, is to design one set of factors to acceptable criteria and the best scheme on the other set then becomes the preferred option. This is a form of goals achievement analysis. This approach is not generally workable at present though, because there are no universal levels of acceptability for either costs or environmental effects as both can vary with location, over time and by viewpoint.

1.3   cont'd

The nearest equivalent to the type of framework that would be suitable for assessing disposal options for colliery spoil is the
Department of Transport's (DTp) framework for trunk road appraisal.
This consists of the economic COBA computer program which uses
social cost-benefit analysis to determine the total costs of
different highway schemes, and the Manual of Environmental
Appraisal (MEA) procedure which summarises the impacts of these
schemes on eleven environmental factors and assesses how these
effects vary for different affected parties.

Other than the COBA results appearing in the summary table of MEA,
no specification is given on how to make a joint evaluation of
economic and environmental impacts. However, some guidance is
given in Advice Note 30/82 "The Choice Between Options for Trunk
Road Schemes". This suggests methods for making the decision
between options more manageable, including pairwise comparison and
trade-off analysis, by comparing options incrementally.

However, there are two important differences relating to spoil
disposal. Firstly, because COBA is dealing with a national investment (a major highway scheme) it has to justify why the preferred
scheme should proceed at all. This is done by testing the options
against a reference scheme which is usually a do-minimum. Such an
approach is not applicable to spoil disposal where a do-minimum
scheme does not exist. Secondly, in the case of major highway
investment there is only one ultimate decision maker: the
Secretary of State for Transport. On the other hand there are at
least two decision makers in spoil disposal issues: NCB in terms
of a commercial decision to proceed; and the MPA (or DoE on
call-in or appeal) in terms of its environmental acceptability via
planning controls. A further important point in this context is
that the different decision makers are likely to place different
weightings on the various decision criteria, whether economic or
environmental. Nevertheless, the DTp framework provided a useful
starting point in the design of an evaluative method which would
reflect the context within which colliery spoil disposal decisions
are made.

C

2.0 ORIGINAL DESIGN OF THE FRAMEWORK

2.1 Introduction

The objectives which lay behind the selected design were to provide a Framework which was:

- comprehensive, so that it could be used to assess options for all types of scheme ranging from an extension of an existing tip to disposal facilities for a new mine;

- flexible, so that it could be adapted for use (e.g. the amount of detail included) as appropriate to the circumstances;

- understandable, so that it could be used and understood by all interested parties;

- clear, so that all the information assembled could be logically and openly presented as a basis for decision making.

It was also intended that the Framework would encourage more dialogue between NCB and MPAs and that both would provide input data.

From an assessment of available techniques of economic and environmental appraisal, it was considered that the Evaluative Framework should be designed to separate NCB costing considerations from the wider effects on the community (loosely termed environmental effects). The Framework has been constructed therefore to include two separate appraisals, which proceed in parallel. The Framework structures the results of each appraisal and brings them together in a combined evaluation without giving particular emphasis to either set.

2.1   cont'd

The Evaluative Framework has therefore been designed to comprise three phases:

Phase I   Selection of Options

Phase II   Cost and Impact Analyses
                      -    Economic
                      -    Environmental

Phase III   Combined Evaluation

Figure 2.1 illustrates the form of the Draft Evaluative Framework as it appeared in the Interim Report April 1984 prior to testing and amendment in the case study programme.

2.2   Phase I

The purpose of Phase I was to provide a procedure for identifying the most realistic options for the disposal of spoil from a particular colliery or development. Figure 2.2 illustrates its original design.

Phase I contains a checklist in questionnaire format designed to make explicit many of the processes that NCB and/or MPA go through already. At the colliery end it requires information on current tipping activity and forecasts of future spoil make. It then requires site specific information on potential disposal locations, which are separated for convenience into local on-site, local off-site and remote.

Three criteria are used in defining feasible options:-

-    technical suitability of handling and transport

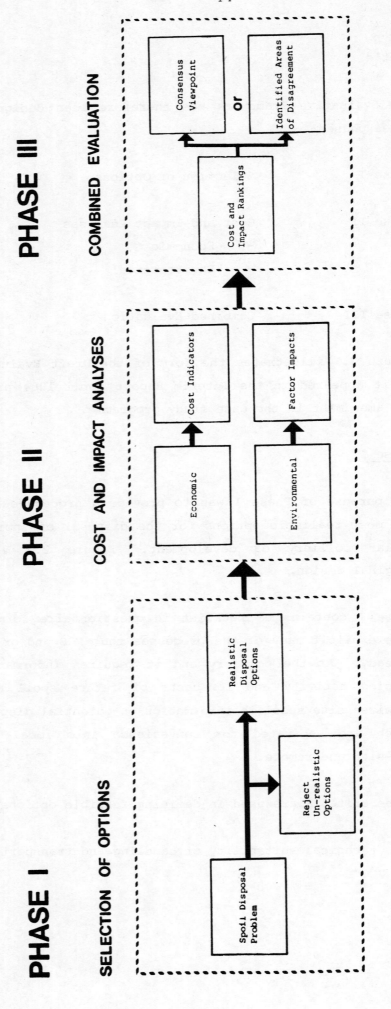

Draft Evaluative Framework

PHASE I — SELECTION OF OPTIONS

PHASE II — COST AND IMPACT ANALYSES

PHASE III — COMBINED EVALUATION

FIGURE 2-1

Draft Evaluative Framework

PHASE I – SELECTION OF OPTIONS

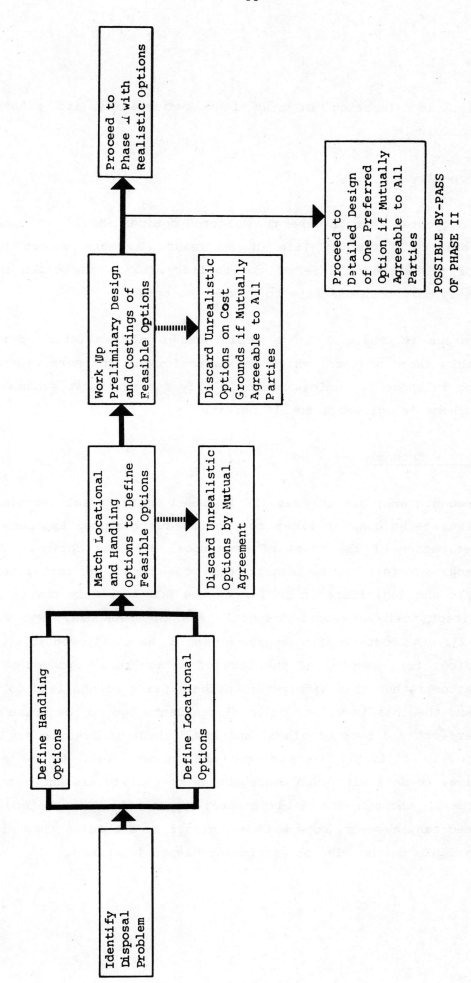

Identify Disposal Problem

Define Handling Options

Define Locational Options

Match Locational and Handling Options to Define Feasible Options

Discard Unrealistic Options by Mutual Agreement

Work Up Preliminary Design and Costings of Feasible Options

Discard Unrealistic Options on Cost Grounds if Mutually Agreeable to All Parties

Proceed to Phase I with Realistic Options

Proceed to Detailed Design of One Preferred Option if Mutually Agreeable to All Parties

POSSIBLE BY-PASS OF PHASE II

FIGURE 2·2

2.2 cont'd

- location (bearing in mind land availability and planning policies)

- capacity.

It is suggested that in general, selected options should be capable of providing a tipping life of at least 20 years unless this exceeds the expected life of the colliery. This may often mean combining more than one site to produce an option.

The output of Phase I is a small number of realistic options (possibly three or four) which are taken forward for more rigorous testing in Phase II, unless there is only one realistic scheme and this scheme is agreeable to all parties.

2.3 Phase II - Economic

The economic analysis in Phase II is based on financial investment appraisal techniques in order to provide a structured approach to the estimation of the costs of each spoil disposal option. This approach was felt to be easier than one based on cost-benefit analysis and legitimate in so far as the NCB currently covers all the direct costs of spoil disposal (see the Financial Review in Part 2). A cost-benefit approach would have allowed for the inclusion, for example, of the loss of agricultural production to the nation rather than simply the purchase price of the land to the NCB, and the loss in value for local residents due to the noise and dust effects and loss of visual amenity. These indirect costs are notoriously difficult to estimate and it was felt to be more practical to deal with such consequences to individuals and society in general through the environmental appraisal. The method as designed can, however, cope with any grants or subsidies that might be available to the NCB for particular disposal schemes.

2.3   cont'd

The Phase II economic appraisal was originally designed in four stages (see Figure 2.3) involving:

-   identifying disposal costs under nine main activity headings via a questionnaire format;

-   assembling capital and operating costs for each activity on a cashflow basis to estimate projected expenditure in each year;

-   discounting cashflows for each option and identifying the Equivalent Annual Cost (EAC) per tonne of spoil and the Initial Capital Cost;

-   summarising cost indicators for each option.

A number of alternative methods by which costs could be analysed were investigated, for example:

-   dividing all costs solely into capital and revenue accounts;

-   categorising all costs by input, for example labour, materials, plant.

These were rejected in favour of the activity based approach.

In addition, a choice had to be made between the use of standardised rates or costing each task in detail. It was decided to include the latter method because of the problems with standardised costings, namely:

-   the difficulties in identifying cost variations peculiar to the particular site under analysis;

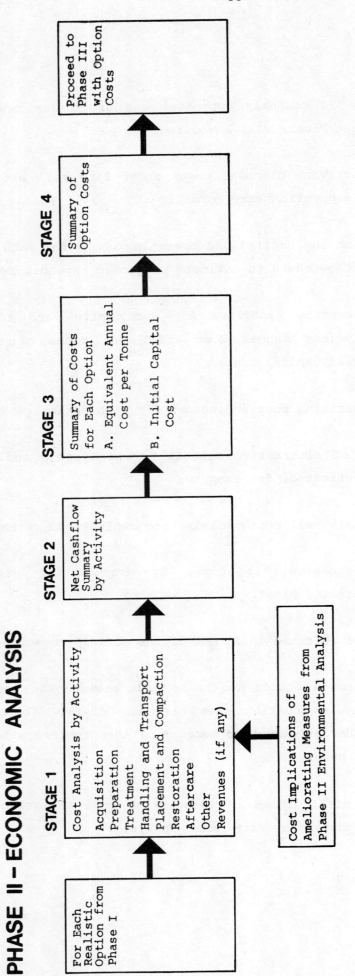

Draft Evaluative Framework

PHASE II – ECONOMIC ANALYSIS

STAGE 1

For Each
Realistic
Option from
Phase I

Cost Analysis by Activity

Acquisition
Preparation
Treatment
Handling and Transport
Placement and Compaction
Restoration
Aftercare
Other
Revenues (if any)

Cost Implications of
Ameliorating Measures from
Phase II Environmental Analysis

STAGE 2

Net Cashflow
Summary
by Activity

STAGE 3

Summary of Costs
for Each Option

A. Equivalent Annual
   Cost per Tonne

B. Initial Capital
   Cost

STAGE 4

Summary of
Option Costs

Proceed to
Phase III
with Option
Costs

FIGURE 2·3

2.3 cont'd

- the difficulties in establishing standard cost values, given that existing operations tend to show wide variations in cost terms;

- the need to update standard costings regularly.

Within each activity heading, therefore, there are questions to identify separately capital and operating account items. The input costs (labour, materials, plant) form part of the background calculations necessary to provide costs for operational items.

The following costs are specifically excluded:

- local colliery overheads, where these will be the same for each alternative. In cases where there is a clear difference, such as by the employment of an extra administrator then such direct costs should be included;

- Area and National NCB overheads, as these ought not to vary as a result of choosing between different alternatives;

- annual depreciation charges. The Framework identifies actual cash outlays to purchase an asset rather than spreading the cost over its useful life;

- interest payments. The use of discounted cashflow automatically allows for interest;

- costs falling onto third parties. Such costs will be covered by virtue of charges to the NCB, such as railway and capital operating costs recovered through BR freight charges;

2.3 cont'd

- rates. Although the NCB's rate bill is assessed to cover all aspects of the industry's activities, its distribution between the local authorities is based on coal production; no such costs therefore bear directly on spoil disposal.

In drawing up a cashflow summary table costs or revenues in different years can be expressed either in real terms, that is in constant money values ignoring inflation, or at out-turn prices with an allowance built in for price changes over time. Techniques exist for handling either approach, but it is generally considered better to eliminate inflation from the analysis and use constant money values.

The base year for constant money purposes was, therefore, taken to be the financial year in which the evaluation is first performed. Account can also be taken in this method of differential inflation between cost items although in practice such changes are difficult to forecast.

In order to compare the cashflows from different options a number of calculations are required. This usually involves bringing all costs and revenues back to present day values. The technique used to do this is to apply a discount rate, which is effectively an interest rate working in reverse. Instead of grossing up present cashflows to allow for interest in subsequent years, the technique discounts future cashflows to bring them to their value today, this being known as their Present Value or PV. Adding together all positive and negative discounted cashflows for a project then gives the Net Present Value or NPV.

The Framework uses a discount rate of 5% because this represents both the NCB's Required Rate of Return on its overall investment programme and, more importantly, that rate to be used in public sector appraisals when choosing between different methods of achieving the same results (Ref. 5).

2.3 cont'd

Two other rates were examined but were felt to be less satisfactory, namely:

-    7%, considered as a generally appropriate rate for appraisal
     in the non-trading public services (e.g. COBA); and

-    10%, being the Board's internal rate for investment decisions.

The particular discount rate can be changed, if required by particular circumstances, without disrupting the Framework.

Although Discounted Cashflow (DCF) techniques are generally
accepted as the most rigorous and theoretically correct methods of
comparing cashflows arising at different points in time, they have
recently been criticised in terms of their application to long life
projects. The problem identified has been the very low Present
Values placed on cashflows arising many years in the future, even
though such cashflows can be very large. Objectors at the Sizewell
B Inquiry, for example, have complained that the technique
discriminates in favour of a nuclear reactor by virtually
eliminating the potentially very large decommissioning costs; as
they arise in say a hundred years time their Present Value is very
low. The objectors have not produced an alternative evaluation
technique which is generally acceptable, however.

Within the DCF methodology there are a variety of potential
outputs. The selected measure for the Framework is the calculation
of a Net Present Value (NPV) for each option. In the case of spoil
disposal schemes, virtually all NPVs will be negative or effectively Net Present Costs (NPCs). Other potential measures from
DCF, including Internal Rates of Return, were considered but were
not considered appropriate for use in the Framework.

2.3 cont'd

The Framework therefore determines NPCs. These cannot be presented as they stand, however, largely because, in a majority of cases, different options will have different capacities and/or lives. Comparing the NPCs of one scheme with say 10mt capacity against one with 100mt capacity may well produce a spurious result and some form of averaging is therefore required.

It is not possible simply to use the NPC/tonne, however, as this would give misleading results for projects with different lives. All other factors being equal the cost in present day terms will decrease as the life of each scheme is extended.

A unit preferable to the NPC is the Equivalent Annual Cost (EAC) which allows a variety of uneven cashflows to be amalgamated into a single simple measure. The EAC is that figure which for each of the years of an option life, when discounted, equals the NPC.

The procedure is therefore to:

-    identify a Net Present Cost for each option;

-    translate this Net Present Cost into an Equivalent Annual Cost over the life of the option (when discounted this equals the same total NPC as the discounted annual cashflows of that option);

-    calculate the average annual amount of solid (or solid and fines) spoil disposed during the life of the option;

-    determine the EAC per tonne disposed, this being calculated as the total Equivalent Annual Cost divided by the average annual tonnage disposed.

2.3 cont'd

The EAC is measured against the tonne of spoil disposed, as opposed to coal, for several reasons:

- Sales of coal vary widely by Area and by colliery. Use of spoil rather than coal enables consistent comparisons to be made whereas the cost related to coal would show greater variation;

- Spoil is the more appropriate measure and bears the direct cost of the disposal operation;

- The NCB already uses costs related to spoil for its own internal uses;

- The Framework is concerned with spoil and not coal. Although additional costs of spoil disposal could be recovered by increases in the price of coal, such activity is external to the Framework and this distinction in costs is maintained.

Notwithstanding this, it is recognised that for some purposes the parties may wish to express the financial costs in terms of saleable output, that is coal. This method of presentation is not precluded by the Framework but merely involves dividing the EAC of each disposal option by the expected average annual output of coal from that colliery.

The use of the DCF technique is different from the normal accruals method used by the NCB to account for current spoil disposal and other production costs. The NCB does use DCF techniques for evaluating between future options and accepts them as the correct basis for use in the Framework. The suggested method does, however, differ from that used in previous spoil disposal analyses, namely the Remote Disposal Working Party set up in connection with the North East Leicestershire coalfield (Ref. 6) and a recent NCB analysis by Butler and Dunn (Ref. 7). These reported option costs in terms of both capital costs and annual operating cost per tonne of spoil, the latter including capital costs by way of a depreciation charge.

2.3 cont'd

Whilst the value of such presentation is recognised, it can present conceptual difficulties. In particular, if the capital costs of a particular alternative are lower than those of another, but the corresponding operating costs are higher, it is difficult to assess which is favoured on economic grounds. The use of DCF techniques will enable this question to be answered unambiguously in such cases.

There may be difficulties in using an approach which implicitly assumes unlimited availability of funds in circumstances where capital investment is limited. The NCB is a Government-owned organisation and, in common with other nationalised industries, is subject to a regime of annual cash limits. In recent years these limits have begun to bite heavily in capital expenditure prog-rammes. It was therefore decided that the Framework should record the initial capital cost of each alternative. It is recognised that use of these costs as a decision criterion could be used to discriminate against schemes with high initial capital costs, even if the EAC is low, but the problem of cash limits has to be recog-nised.

Other measures were considered for incorporation in the Framework, namely first year effect on NCB's profit and loss account, and pay-back. Both were rejected, however, the former because an indiv-idual scheme is unlikely to have any influence on the Board's operation as a whole and the latter because spoil disposal is not an activity which produces significant revenues compared with costs.

2.4   Phase II - Environmental

The purpose of the Phase II environmental assessment was to provide a comprehensive examination of all of the environmental impacts which vary between the disposal options under consideration. It was felt that the type of assessment in the Framework needed to go further than the NCB's environmental checklist procedure. The Framework therefore, not only gives guidance on the techniques for measuring each environmental impact but also highlights the effects on different parties. Moreover, the analysis is intended to be used openly at an early stage as a way of testing different options, instead of providing a later test to ensure that all factors have been covered before presentation of a preferred option.

The environmental assessment was originally designed in three stages (see Figure 2.4) involving:

- assessing the existing environmental quality of the proposed tipping site and surroundings and any transport route required;

- assessing the projected impacts of each option on a range of environmental criteria highlighting parties affected and changes over time;

- summarising the effects of each option on those environmental factors where there is a significant difference in impact.

The first two stages were set out in questionnaire format ending in short summaries of the information collected for each option. It was envisaged that the work would be undertaken as a desk study with some field work as necessary. Detailed study sheets were provided for recording working notes, especially those made out on site. The summaries were intended to include short factual statements on each factor, with quantification of elements where applicable.

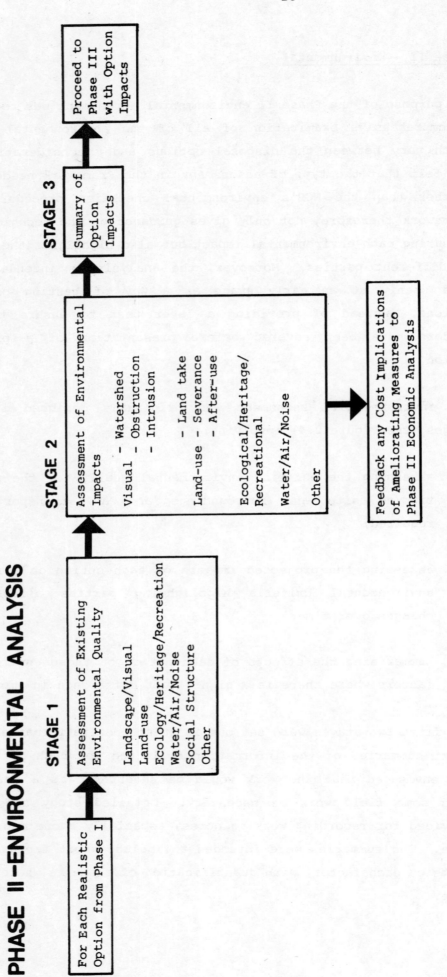

Draft Evaluative Framework

PHASE II—ENVIRONMENTAL ANALYSIS

STAGE 1

For Each Realistic Option from Phase I

Assessment of Existing Environmental Quality

Landscape/Visual
Land-use
Ecology/Heritage/Recreation
Water/Air/Noise
Social Structure
Other

STAGE 2

Assessment of Environmental Impacts

Visual – Watershed
– Obstruction
– Intrusion

– Land take
Land-use – Severance
– After-use

Ecological/Heritage/Recreational

Water/Air/Noise

Other

Feedback any Cost Implications of Ameliorating Measures to Phase II Economic Analysis

STAGE 3

Summary of Option Impacts

Proceed to Phase III with Option Impacts

FIGURE 2·4

2.4 cont'd

Six aspects of the existing environment were considered necessary to cover in the first questionnaire. An appraisal of existing disposal operations would be included for options involving tip extensions. Subjective judgements are involved to a much greater extent with environmental assessment than with economic appraisal.

The impacts of spoil disposal were seen to fall into four main headings:-

-   visual

-   land use

-   ecological/heritage/recreational

-   pollutants (water, air, noise).

No attempt was made to rank the importance of these impacts as this will vary both with the particular scheme and with the subjective viewpoint of the observer. For example, the two most fundamental issues related to the NCB's tipping proposals at the Vale of Belvoir Inquiry were the visual impact and agricultural land take of the proposed spoil tips. Most impacts, but particularly those arising under the heading of pollutants, should be capable of being reduced to acceptable limits through good practice backed up by planning controls where ameliorating measures can be taken. This may, in turn, have implications for the cost of the option under consideration.

Various techniques and data sources were suggested for the assessment of impacts together with guidance on the units of measurement most appropriate.

D

2.4 cont'd

The Framework also recognised that different parties are subjected to different impacts depending on their proximity to disposal operations and that impacts vary through the life of a scheme. Summary tables, therefore, required assessment on each environmental factor, for each affected party and, for both the operational and after-use stages.   Affected parties were considered to be:

- residents and other occupiers;

- landowners;

- recreation users;

- travellers.

For the final summary of option impacts it was considered preferable to structure this by environmental factor rather than commenting on the combined effects on each of the affected parties.

2.5 Phase III

The aim of Phase III was to present the information on options in a manageable form to assist decision making but not necessarily to produce a decision. It brings together for testing the predominantly commercial criterion of the NCB against the predominantly environmental impacts which spoil disposal has on the community directly affected. To assist the process three decision aiding tools were included, capable of being used on their own or in combination. The idea of mechanistically trying to convert the environmental impacts into monetary terms in a Roskill-type exercise was firmly rejected. The original design is shown in Figure 2.5.

Draft Evaluative Framework

PHASE III – COMBINED EVALUATION

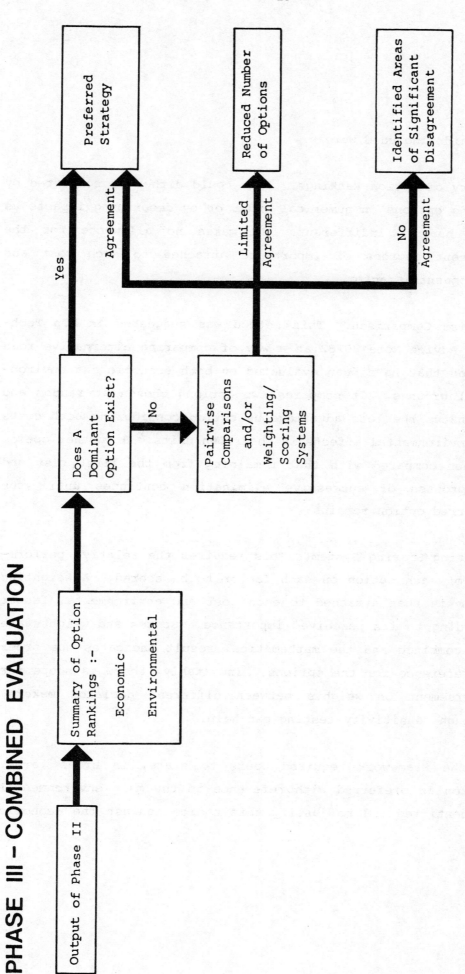

FIGURE 2·5

2.5 cont'd

The three aids included were:

- Summary of Option Rankings. This could either be completed by ranking options in numerical order or by describing impacts as good, bad or indifferent. It makes no allowance for the different degrees of importance attached to each cost and environmental factor.

- Pairwise Comparison. This method was suggested in DTp Technical Advice Note 30/82 as a way of comparing alternative road schemes that have been evaluated on both economic and environmental grounds. It compares two options chosen at random and eliminates the less advantageous option considering both costs and environmental effects in their own units. A further option is then compared with that remaining from the first test and the process of successive elimination continues until the preferred option remains.

- Weighting/Scoring System. This requires the relative performance of each option on each factor to be scored. A weighting system is then attached to each cost and environmental factor according to its perceived importance. Scores and weights are then combined and the mathematical result indicates the order of preference for the options. Inevitably, there is scope for disagreement on weights between different decision makers, although sensitivity testing can help.

Finally, the Framework required users to state, in brief terms, which option is preferred with reference to the main environmental effects identified and to justify this choice against the economic costs.

2.5 cont'd

Each of these three techniques were seen as decision <u>aiding</u> tools
with a trade-off still needing to be made by decision makers on the
key issues before selecting the preferred option. It must be
remembered that the Framework has been designed to aid decision
making between options. Whether or not the preferred option should
proceed is an issue subsequent to the use of the Framework.

3.0 TESTING THE FRAMEWORK

3.1 The Case Study Programme

A Draft Evaluative Framework (DEF) was published as part of the Consultants' Interim Report in April 1984. This was compiled into a self-contained volume complete with a full set of study sheets before the start of the case study programme which ran from May 1984 to September 1985. Twelve case studies were completed over that period, some of which were conducted concurrently where they covered related topics.

The format and content of the DEF was revised sequentially during the first six case studies, after which a more general review took place. This resulted in the preparation of the Interim Evaluative Framework (IEF) in February 1985 together with a draft Manual containing guidance on how to complete the questions and the most appropriate circumstances for its use. An updated version of the IEF was produced in April 1985 which expanded the guidance notes and incorporated them into the Framework for easier reference, and made the Framework applicable to sea-based options as well as land-based. The final version of the Framework and Manual was prepared in September 1985.

The twelve completed case studies are listed in Table 3.1. Most of the schemes had been chosen before the Research Project started and had been carefully selected to reflect different types of spoil disposal, with an emphasis on different handling and transport solutions. The locations of the schemes were also well spread within the Yorks, Notts, Derby coalfield to ensure contact with as many of the County Councils and NCB Area offices as possible. One scheme was located in South Wales because it was the best example of a current disposal scheme dependent on rail transport. Two schemes from the original Terms of Reference were replaced by other schemes in the same locality where decisions were pending as it was felt that the results of the case studies could be put to some practical use.

TABLE 3.1

DESCRIPTION OF CASE STUDIES

SCHEME	LOCATION	TYPE OF DISPOSAL SITE	HANDLING & TRANSPORT
1. Dinnington	S. Yorks Area S. Yorks CC	Extension to local tipping site, including lagoons	Dump trucks on internal haul road.
2. South Kirkby	Barnsley Area W. Yorks CC	Tip extension v. landfill reclamation site (Welbeck)	Stacker spreader (extension) v. 17km rail (landfill)
3. Woolley	Barnsley Area W. Yorks CC	Tip extension v. landfill reclamation site (Welbeck)	Dumptrucks/ Stacker spreader (extension) v. 15km rail (landfill)
4. Maltby	S. Yorks Area S. Yorks CC	Adjacent limestone quarry (operational)	Cable belt
5. Bentinck	S. Notts Area Notts CC	Tip extension partly over opencast site	Conveyor
6. Gedling (Fines only)	S. Notts Area Notts CC	Worked out sand and gravel pits	4km pipeline
7. Nelson Bog	S. Wales Area Mid Glamorgan CC	Low-lying wet valley land	5km rail and dump trucks on internal road
8. Glews Hollow	Doncaster Area S. Yorks CC Boothferry DC	Wet reclamation site	14km rail, 23km canal v. 25km road
9. Asfordby	S. Midlands Area Leicestershire CC	Valley site v. 2 derelict voids + 2 operational voids	Conveyor v. 37 or 58km road, 60km rail, 100km rail, 200km rail
10. Pyewipe	Humberside CC	Reclamation of mudflats	100km rail v road, canal/river
11. Gale Common	N. Yorks Area West Yorks CC	Low-lying farmland Bank construction for pfa lagoon	12km hydraulic pipeline (pfa), 8km road (spoil)
12. Allerton Bywater	N. Yorks Area W. Yorks CC	Opencast void	4km road then barge

3.1 cont'd

Each of the case studies was used by the Consultants to test different aspects of the Framework. Lessons were also drawn for spoil
disposal practice where possible and these have been incorporated
in Part 2 of this report.

3.2 Methods of Working

The method of conducting the case studies also varied during the
programme. In general, after an introductory meeting with the
relevant NCB Area, the current draft of Phases I and II of the
Framework was left for the NCB to complete. A follow up meeting
was then used to discuss the results and reactions to the
methodology in general. Further amendments to the results were
then made as required. Meetings were also held with the relevant
Local Authorities and for one study, the MPA filled in the environmental summary to give a different perspective. For the two case
studies where decisions were imminent, the Consultants played a
more active role in sorting out the issues, collecting data from
both the NCB and MPA and then filling in the questionnaires. For
other case studies that involved future schemes it was also the
Consultants that filled in the Framework.

Meetings with other bodies were also held where necessary to
provide information to complete the questionnaires: such as MAFF,
Water Authorities, Opencast and Minestone Executives. Background
literature was consulted as appropriate.

Most of the case studies included field work although this was less
effective than hoped because of the concurrent mine workers
industrial dispute. In particular, it was not possible to complete
any measurements of possible pollutants such as noise and dust
although these techniques are well documented. Having established
a sound design of the DEF some of the later case studies (which
were proposed schemes) were conducted as desk studies.

3.2   cont'd

The testing of the Phase III decision aiding techniques was carried out as an internal team exercise for those case studies that provided options.   It had been hoped to involve the NCB and MPA in a simulated decision making exercise towards the end of the case study programme but this did not prove possible in practice for a variety of reasons.   Instead, the results of the most extensive test were discussed at a seminar attended by a University Professor specialising in environmental issues and a Department of the Environment representative.

Individual case study reports were prepared as working tools during the course of the project.   The emphasis in preparing these was not on describing accurately all the details of the particular scheme under investigation but rather on using the studies to test different aspects of the Framework and to report on successive amendments.   The way in which each of the case studies was used is described in Table 3.2.   This process also allowed the client steering bodies and the participants of each case study to provide feedback on conclusions reached during the course of the study.

The early case studies (Dinnington, Maltby, Bentinck and Gedling) were used to test the comprehensiveness of the economic and environmental questionnaires included in Phase II of the Framework at different types of disposal site (local tip extension and various forms of void) and using different equipment (dump trucks, conveyor, pipeline).   All these studies were based on historical schemes where there had been no obvious options to be tested. Different forms of illustrating the visual effects of a scheme were also tested including Visual Envelope Maps (VEM), sections, photomontages and artists perspectives.   Attention was also paid to the best way of summarising the information from the environmental assessment.

TABLE 3.2   THE ROLE OF EACH CASE STUDY IN
                   TESTING THE FRAMEWORK

Scheme	Historical/ Projected	On-site/ Off-site Options	Focus for testing Evaluative Framework
1. Dinnington	Historical	On-site	Phase II economic and environmental question- naires VEM, sections, photomontage
2. South Kirkby	Projected	On-site v Off-site Option	Phase I questionnaire Phase II summaries Cross-subsidy from other materials
3. Woolley	"		Artists perspective Phase III Weighting/Scoring System
4. Maltby	Historical	Local Off-site	Phase II summaries VEM, sections
5. Bentinck	Historical	On-site	Meetings with
6. Gedling	Historical	Local Off-site	MAFF Water Authority Opencast Executive
7. Nelson Bog	Historical	Local Off-site v. 2 hypo- thetical options	Phase I questionnaire Phase II summaries Phase III Pairwise Comparison
8. Glews Hollow	Projected	Off-site (3 transport options)	Phase I questionnaire Phase II summaries Effect on EAC of indus- trial after-use value Phase III Option Rankings
9. Asfordby	Projected	On-site v. 4 off-site options	Phase II summaries Phase III all 3 techniques & associated statements
10. Pyewipe	Projected	Off-site	Use of EF for reception sites Phase I questionnaire Phase II summaries
11. Gale Common*	Historical	Off-site	Costs and information from NCB Background only
12. Allerton Bywater	Projected	Off-site	Final check of questionn- aires

* This scheme in conjunction with the CEGB was not covered as a full case
study.

3.2   cont'd

The emphasis of the remaining case studies was on the selection of
options (Phase I) and the evaluation of options (Phase III) for
particular disposal problems.

The South Kirkby and Woolley studies provided an opportunity of
working up illustrative options for local tipping to be compared
against a single off-site option at Welbeck. The first test of the
usefulness of decision aiding techniques was then made using the
Weighting/Scoring system. The Nelson Bog case study, as well as
providing an historical check of rail transport impacts, was also
used to test the Pairwise Comparison technique using two
hypothetical options generated by the research team. The Glews
Hollow scheme provided an opportunity of testing three alternative
transport modes from the originating colliery (Hatfield) to the
projected reception site using the Option Rankings technique.

The Asfordby case study provided the most complete test of the
combined evaluation phase of the Framework where all three decision
aiding techniques were tested against one local and four remote
options.

4.0 AMENDING THE FRAMEWORK

4.1 Introduction

The Framework was refined successively throughout the case study programme by a certain amount of restructuring, clarification of techniques and by adding or amending individual questions. The basic design of a three part process comprising: identification of options, a parallel assessment of direct costs and wider environmental consequences, and lastly a combined evaluation, remained firmly intact.

This chapter deals with each of the three phases in turn describing firstly the more important changes of a restructuring nature (mainly confined to the Phase II environmental section), and secondly summarising the detailed changes to the constituent questionnaires and/or assessment techniques. A full description of the final Framework is given in the accompanying Manual. A summary chart of the final content of the three phased procedure is shown in Figure 4.1 and each of the individual phases in Figures 4.2 to 4.5.

15.2 Phase I

No major restructuring occurred and the procedure remained as a questionnaire format under five main headings:

1. Identify disposal problem

2. Define handling options

3. Define locational options

4. Match preliminary locational and handling options

5. Work up preliminary design and costings for each feasible option.

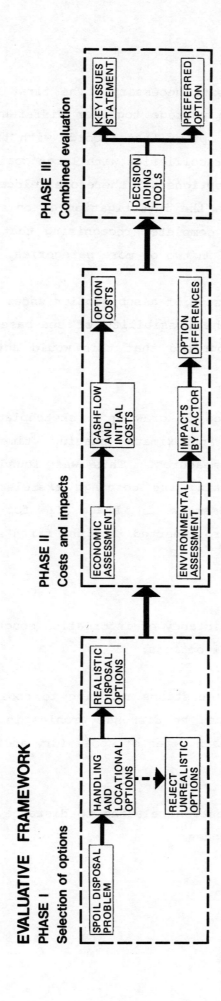

FIGURE 4·1

4.2 cont'd

There were three main amendments necessary. The first related to the possibility of having to package together different disposal sites in order to produce an option that accords with the 20 year tipping capacity guideline for collieries with large coal reserves. The definition of locational options was therefore relocated at the end of the third section when the investigation of on-site, local off-site and remote sites is complete, recognising that an option will sometimes comprise sites in two or more categories.

The second involved the inclusion of a sub-section under local off-site options to allow for the possibility of sea-based disposal schemes although it was recognised that this would not often be required.

The third related to the need to draw up a sketchplan for each option together with an approximate phasing timetable and indication of amelioration measures. This was found to be a necessary prelude to completing the costings exercise and site specific environmental assessment in Phase II for projected schemes, and this was therefore inserted into the fifth section.

Other detailed changes were:

- revisions to ensure consistency of information sought on the three types of locational options;

- sub-division of certain questions relating to spoil make and capacities to ensure that the disposal problem is identified separately for the two main types of spoil (dry and wet) where appropriate;

- repositioning of the question relating to distance thresholds of available transport modes;

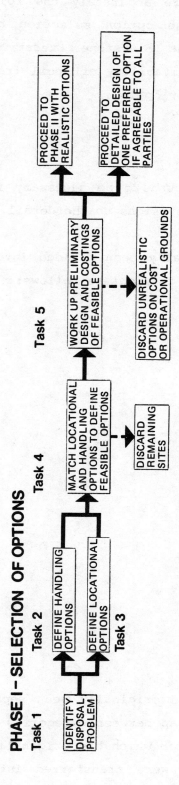

PHASE I – SELECTION OF OPTIONS

Task 1 — IDENTIFY DISPOSAL PROBLEM

Task 2 — DEFINE HANDLING OPTIONS

Task 3 — DEFINE LOCATIONAL OPTIONS

Task 4 — MATCH LOCATIONAL AND HANDLING OPTIONS TO DEFINE FEASIBLE OPTIONS

DISCARD REMAINING SITES

Task 5 — WORK UP PRELIMINARY DESIGN AND COSTINGS OF FEASIBLE OPTIONS

DISCARD UNREALISTIC OPTIONS ON COST OR OPERATIONAL GROUNDS

PROCEED TO PHASE II WITH REALISTIC OPTIONS

PROCEED TO DETAILED DESIGN OF ONE PREFERRED OPTION IF AGREEABLE TO ALL PARTIES

FIGURE 4.2

4.2 cont'd

- revisions to portray more accurately the role of MAFF and Water Authorities in the option selection process and an addition to mention the Minestone Executive who may be required to check the suitability of spoil from a particular colliery for a reclamation option.

4.3 <u>Phase II - Economic</u>

No major restructuring was found to be necessary in this section although there were several revisions to the detail.

The cost analysis had originally been divided into nine activity headings. These were reduced to eight as follows:

1. Acquisition

2. Preparation

3. Treatment

4. Handling and Transport

5. Placement and Compaction

6. Restoration and Aftercare

7. Other

8. Revenues

Restoration and aftercare had originally been separated but were combined because of the overlap between categories of expenditure. The costs of a stacker spreader which had originally been included in Placement and Compaction were transferred into Handling and Transport where they more logically fit.

- 43 -

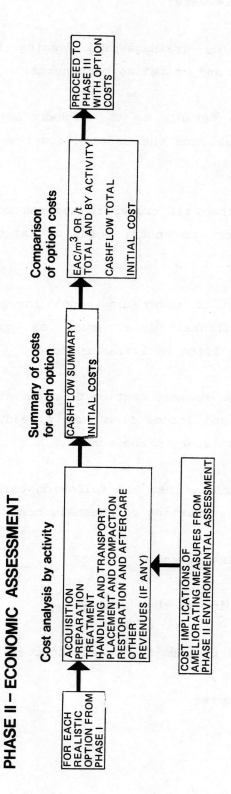

FIGURE 4.3

4.3 cont'd

Minor changes to the questionnaire were:

- sub-division of questions on drainage and fencing in the second section into capital and operating components;

- repositioning of any costs payable to the Highway Authority for road improvement schemes from the second into the fourth category;

- inclusion of questions in the rail transport section covering emergency storage facilities and annual costs of maintaining rail wagons;

- inclusion of a sub-section to cover any costs involved in reclamation to non-agricultural uses, such as grading, levelling, drainage and provision of infrastructure;

- addition of questions in the revenue section to cover terminal value of any mobile plant and income from land already owned by NCB but not needed until later in the scheme.

Early in the testing it became clear that the following parameters need to be clearly defined before starting to assemble costs:

- start and end date of tipping scheme;

- time horizon of costs relating to that scheme;

- start point in the disposal process for measuring costs;

- date at which prices are quoted.

4.3 cont'd

Guidance notes were provided in the draft Manual, together with notes on how to avoid the inclusion of "sunk costs" that is those incurred in cash terms at some previous date in relation to another scheme, and to avoid double counting of costs particularly with reference to the different ways in which NCB Areas account for their surface mobile plant charges.

The cashflow summary procedure has basically remained the same throughout the testing programme. The definition of the first year was changed to the first year in which costs are incurred so that advance costs can be treated on a year by year basis rather than included as a lump sum in the first year of tipping. This has implications for the reporting of capital costs which had originally been specified as those occurring in the first five years of a scheme. Discussion with the NCB confirmed that this period has little significance unless the scheme has an imminent start date in which case it corresponds to the five year time horizon over which NCB capital allocations are made. A more relevant definition was seen to be all the initial capital costs required to get the scheme going and in most cases this will equate to capital spent up to and including the first year of tipping.

Several refinements have been made to the calculation of the EAC/t formula, namely:-

-       the inclusion of an adjustment factor to allow the formula to cope with schemes where the first year of tipping is some time after the first year of relevant cashflow;

-       the introduction of separate calculations to give the EAC/t for each activity heading in order to focus attention on the main areas of difference between the options.

It was also felt that the cashflow total should be reported as an indicator of the total sums of money involved over the life of a scheme.

4.3 cont'd

There was also considerable discussion as to whether the reporting
of the EAC per annual spoil disposed should be per tonne or per m³.
Both have relevance, in that capacities of land areas and voids are
usually assessed in volume terms (m³) whereas transport costs are
usually calculated in weight terms (tonnes). The per tonne measure
also allows a more ready comparison between spoil disposal costs,
and total production and selling costs of coal. The most appropriate measure should therefore be used for the project in hand. If
no local factor is available for the particular colliery, conversion can be made assuming an average of 1.75 tonnes per m³.

There was also a suggestion from NCB Finance Department during the
case study programme that the EAC formula was needlessly complicated and that the average annual cashflow measure would be
adequate in most cases.

By its nature, the EAC is likely to give a similar result to an
average annual cashflow if:

-       capital costs are either low or are spread evenly over a
        project life;

-       operating costs are constant each year;

-       the project has a reasonably long life.

Similar results are not necessarily obtained if these circumstances
do not hold. The example in Appendix C indicates a difference of
10% between a straight average annual cashflow and the (correct)
EAC. Other examples can be identified which show an even greater
divergence.

The use of a simple average is not preferred, therefore, for the
following reasons:

4.3 cont'd

- although there are cases where it gives a figure which corresponds closely to the EAC, this is not always so;

- in practice, the convenience of using a simple average is more apparent than real. Most of the work in the economic evaluation is concerned with producing the cashflow tables. Once produced, the calculation of EAC is trivial, especially if micro-computer aids are used;

- it would be very difficult at a Public Inquiry to defend a criterion which was essential to the decision making process but which was theoretically weak.

By the half way stage in the testing programme, two computer packages had been developed, one by the Consultants and the other by NCB Operational Research Executive (ORE), to take the tedium out of the discounting and EAC calculations.

Both operate on an IBM Personal Computer and are based on a Lotus 1-2-3 spreadsheet package. The package produced by the NCB ORE was set up to be menu driven and had an accompanying manual to make it self-explanatory to NCB Area personnel. Both packages contain the individual question numbers and topics relating to the cost questionnaire on the vertical axis with the timespan of individual years on the horizontal axis, thus condensing the first two stages of the analysis and replacing the working sheets previously necessary to produce the cashflow summary. Both programs automatically transfer the input data to the cost indicator summary tables and calculate the EAC/tonne.

The Consultants' package operated on a single spreadsheet rather than being divided into individual screens for each cost category. It was therefore quicker to operate and effective as a means of sensitivity testing. It also produced the EAC/tonne of each activity as a standard output. The ORE package, however, distinguished capital and operating costs more clearly.

4.3 cont'd

In addition, there were minor differences between the packages in the formula used to calculate the EAC. The two formulae produced the same answer when the quantity of spoil tipped is the same each year of a scheme but the ORE formula was more rigorous when signif-icant variations are forecast to occur.

The best elements of each package were eventually combined for use with the Evaluative Framework, although the calculations can be performed manually if preferred.

4.4 Phase II - Environmental

Restructuring was necessary in this section of the Framework because, in practice, the previous two part questionnaire separ-ating a description of the existing situation from project impact, was found to contain too much duplication. The format was therefore condensed into one questionnaire but in the main retained the same information requirement, the existing situation being seen as necessary context for the assessment of impact.

The detailed study sheets were also abandoned after the first six case studies. These had originally been seen as a transition between the questionnaires and the summary tables. It was found to be possible to short-cut this part of the process thus making the Framework far more compact (the detailed sheets had originally amounted to about 40 pages).

The abandonment of the study sheets went in hand with the expansion of the summary sheets. The latter had originally been drawn up to include one word descriptions of the severity of impact on each environmental factor for each affected party, such as good, bad, marginal. This was found to be too limiting.

4.4 cont'd

The summary sheets were therefore expanded to include details for each of the environmental factors, of:

-   the date/timing of each impact;

-   the quantity and scale of features affected;

-   the different parties affected.

For case studies later in the testing programme, impact summary sheets occupied up to four pages compared to the single sheet originally envisaged.

The revised method of summarising impacts provided a much easier transfer of information to the final summary sheet in Phase II which compares the differences in impacts for each of the options under investigation. It also made the whole process more compatible with the sequence in the Phase II economic appraisal.

The final summary sheet was also expanded and its focus set on describing option differences rather than stating impacts. Three additional columns were added to provide a better transition into the combined evaluation phase. These were:

-   an indication of whether the differences identified were significant;

-   a statement of which option was least affected environmentally, in the event of significant differences;

-   a similar statement of which option was worst affected.

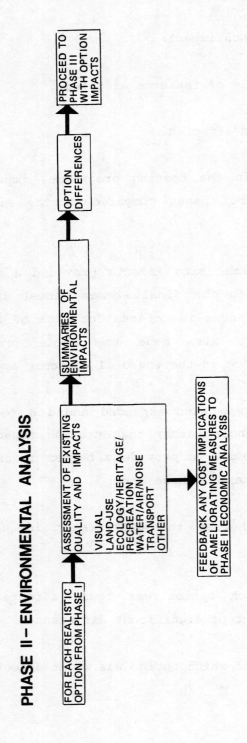

PHASE II – ENVIRONMENTAL ANALYSIS

FOR EACH REALISTIC OPTION FROM PHASE I

ASSESSMENT OF EXISTING QUALITY AND IMPACTS

VISUAL
LAND-USE
ECOLOGY/HERITAGE/
RECREATION
WATER/AIR/NOISE
TRANSPORT
OTHER

FEEDBACK ANY COST IMPLICATIONS OF AMELIORATING MEASURES TO PHASE II ECONOMIC ANALYSIS

SUMMARIES OF ENVIRONMENTAL IMPACTS

OPTION DIFFERENCES

PROCEED TO PHASE III WITH OPTION IMPACTS

FIGURE 4.4

4.4 cont'd

Within the revised environmental questionnaire factors were regrouped under six main headings:

1. Visual
2. Land Use
3. Ecological/Heritage/Recreational
4. Pollutants
5. Transport Route
6. Other.

Visual impacts had originally been seen as comprising three main components: watershed, obstruction and intrusion. These terms caused confusion and had to be clarified and simplified. The first term was intended to identify the degree of containment of a scheme on a particular site as measured by the Visual Envelope Map (VEM). The second sought to identify which views (if any) might be blocked by a scheme and the third assessed the degree of intrusiveness of the scheme. Questions were retained on each aspect with the visual envelope being given greater emphasis at the data gathering stage.

Severance had originally been seen as a separate category of land use impact in the summary reporting. It was later subsumed into the general assessment of land use effects in the operational stage. Social structure, previously a small section describing the existing context, was combined with other general questions about the site into the visual section.

Transport route (applicable to off-site options) was added as an additional environmental factor to be assessed taking account of the level of traffic increase (or usage if new), the number of sensitive properties along the route and the degree of conflict (if any) with other traffic.

4.4 cont'd

Detailed changes which were made to the environmental questionnaire were:

- extension of the question on existing trees to cover all tree cover and not just those covered by Tree Preservation Orders;

- inclusion of a question to cover the specific impact of lagoons within a tipping scheme, where applicable;

- inclusion of a question to give details of any special ameliorating features of a scheme, such as screening mounds, tree screens or other planting;

- additional questions to quantify the area and use of land required for the site and the proposed after-use;

- addition of questions relating to restoration proposals and the availability of top-soil and sub-soil for feasible restoration to agricultural use;

- inclusion of a sub-section to cover the environmental impacts of sea-based options, including effect on fisheries;

- reference to schemes which incorporate GDO tips as part of the future tipping programme and restoration proposals, with questions on area of tip involved and the scope for improvement;

- deletion of question seeking an estimate of current crop yields on the basis that this is difficult to provide and validate, and that the inherent qualities of the land (that is its agricultural land classification grade) are of far greater importance.

4.4 cont'd

Various refinements were made to the form of assessment technique considered most appropriate for use in the Framework. In particular, the construction of the VEM was made more sophisticated to exclude shadow areas from which a view of the tip may be obscured by changes in ground level or partially screened by trees or buildings. For the purposes of impact assessment, property counts can be made within different distance bands of the site (within ½km, 1km, 2km) with greater weight usually being placed on those affected within the closest bands. In some topographical conditions, however, the visual effects may be more noticeable from afar than in the immediate locality. The extent of the VEM around a void can also be misleading because the impact is unlikely to be significant except where the site is overlooked from high ground.

Photomontages were found to be a useful way of illustrating the scale of a projected tip on the landscape. Where this technique is used, the same photo should be used for the before and after view to ensure the same scale and content. Where sections are used, the same scale should be used for vertical and horizontal axes.

It was not possible to test the mechanics of measuring existing noise and dust levels in the field because of the industrial action during most of the case study programme. However, these methods are well documented elsewhere, and in most cases their use would not be appropriate in any event. Such examination might only be necessary where this topic was a source of major disagreement at a Public Inquiry.

4.5 Phase III

Considerable refinement was made to the suggested way in which the decision aiding tools might be used during the case study programme and in the final drafting of the Framework the Weighting/Scoring system was excluded.

4.5   cont'd

The Weighting/Scoring system had attracted a fair amount of scepticism throughout the case study programme. The main concerns were
that it involved:

-   making unrealistic assumptions about the distribution of
    weights;

-   putting numerical values on the difference between options
    which, for most of the environmental factors, were expressed
    in descriptive terms only;

-   producing figure work which looked seemingly simple but, if
    not interpreted carefully, could easily be misunderstood;

-   using a technique which did not have a strong theoretical
    basis.

Various refinements were made during the case study programme to
try to reduce these concerns, namely:

-   each party allocating weights (100 rather than 50) according
    to the relative importance attached to each factor, independ-
    ently of the options under consideration to exclude the risk
    of double counting differences between options;

-   sensitivity testing to illustrate the effects of different
    allocations of weights between the economic and environmental
    groups of factors (the construction of a graph was suggested);

-   noting on an accompanying statement the reasons why a part-
    icular set of weights had been selected for that exercise and
    how the scores had been allocated between options;

-   allocating scores ranging from 1 (worst option) to 10 (best
    option) on each environmental factor rather than trying to
    distribute and correctly balance a total of 20 points between
    options.

4.5 cont'd

Appendix D records the final form of the Weighting/Scoring system table and sensitivity graph before they were excluded from the Framework.

The main problem that the technique could not overcome was the reconciliation of different value judgements on the relative importance of economic and environmental factors in one weighting system. Cost benefit techniques attempt to do this by reducing all factors to common monetary values. This approach was, however, rejected at the beginning of the Framework's development. In order to overcome this concern the Consultants advocated using, as a starting point, a "neutral" distribution of 50 weights to economic factors and 50 to environmental factors, and then sensitivity testing the result on different weighting systems. This approach was not acceptable to the NCB who still maintained that the technique was not suitable for combining the preferences of organisations with different responsibilities and objectives.

Other parties were still concerned about the impression of spurious accuracy that the technique gave and the danger that the exercise of using it could degenerate into a numbers game. It was therefore decided to exclude it from the final version of the Evaluative Framework.

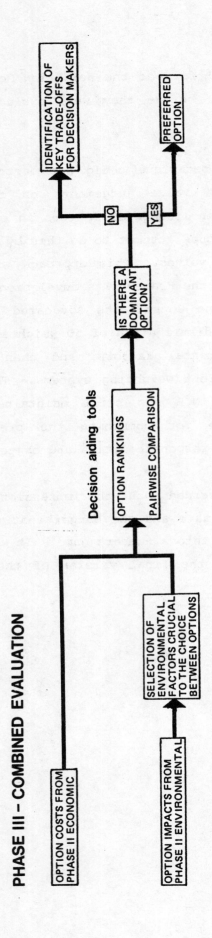

PHASE III – COMBINED EVALUATION

OPTION COSTS FROM
PHASE II ECONOMIC

OPTION IMPACTS FROM
PHASE II ENVIRONMENTAL

SELECTION OF
ENVIRONMENTAL
FACTORS CRUCIAL
TO THE CHOICE
BETWEEN OPTIONS

Decision aiding tools

OPTION RANKINGS

PAIRWISE COMPARISON

IS THERE A
DOMINANT
OPTION?

NO

YES

IDENTIFICATION OF
KEY TRADE-OFFS
FOR DECISION MAKERS

PREFERRED
OPTION

FIGURE 4.5

4.5 cont'd

In terms of the Phase III process, two additional elements were added namely:

- an opening statement to focus onto the key environmental factors in terms of comparing the particular set of options under consideration;

- a key issues statement as a final summary of the procedure focusing attention on the main trade-offs to be made by decision makers.

Changes made to the two remaining decision aiding techniques were as follows:

Option Rankings - it was considered better to indicate the preference of options graphically by the use of stars or a symbol of some type (giving a high indicator to good options). This ensures that no-one tries to total up the numbers given to each option as they might if each option had been ranked in numerical order against each environmental factor. Such a procedure could give a misleading impression of accuracy in that a total of straight rankings would take no account of the relative importance of each factor.

Pairwise Comparison - the emphasis of the process was found to be more appropriately placed on eliminating options rather than selecting one preferred option. Larger boxes were required in the presentation to allow brief reasons to be recorded for preferences made. A need was also identified to reiterate the comparisons between options that had not been eliminated until all pairings had been completed. Provided that this was done it did not matter in which order options were taken.

5.0 APPRAISAL OF THE EVALUATIVE FRAMEWORK

5.1 Introduction

This section assesses how well the Evaluative Framework in its final form fulfils the objectives set out at the beginning of the design process. These were that the Framework should be:

- comprehensive

- flexible

- understandable

- clear.

Three wider issues are then briefly explored which have been raised from time to time in the various discussions held during the case study programme. These are:

- does the Framework go too far into the decision making process, that is, does it need the combined evaluation techniques (Phase III)?

- how feasible is the principle of joint working as intended by the Framework?

- is the Framework really required, that is, has it all been worth it?

It is acknowledged that there will be a need to monitor and further refine the Framework as it is used in practice.

5.2 Fulfilment of Objectives

The four stated objectives are examined in turn:

- Comprehensiveness

    In general the Framework has stood up well on this criterion.
    The original design sought to include questions to cover as
    many types of colliery disposal site locations, handling
    equipment and modes of transport as possible. Various
    additions were then made during the testing process to include
    different types of after-use (industrial as well as agricul-
    tural), and sea-based as well as land-based disposal options.
    The Framework was shown to be reversible in that it can be
    used (with slight amendments to Phase I) to test the best
    choice of originating colliery(ies) to provide spoil for a
    particular reception site as well as disposal options for a
    particular colliery.

    The final Framework is therefore tried and tested to deal with
    a range of circumstances including:

    - existing collieries or new mines;

    - local tip extensions or off-site locations (voids, low-
      lying or other reclamation sites);

    - schemes including lagoons as well as dry tipping;

    - sea-based as well as land-based disposal schemes;

    - different handling equipment (for example conveyors,
      surface mobile plant);

    - different transport modes (road, rail, canal, pipeline,
      conveyor);

F

5.2 cont'd

- sites owned by the NCB, other mineral operators, or other agencies;

- spoil tipping as the sole activity or co-disposal with other materials or other concurrent operations such as opencast mining;

- schemes involving different sources of revenue after completion;

- schemes involving some grant aid, contribution from other parties or cross-subsidisation to reduce operating costs.

The Framework does not in its present form allow comparison of disposal options with a commercial use for spoil or underground stowage. It could be readily adapted if necessary.

In order to be this comprehensive the Framework has to be relatively bulky, although it has been considerably reduced in length during the testing process. In practice the questionnaires have been found to be quick to operate by simply striking through all the sections that do not apply to the project under consideration.

As a guide to the amount of time taken in filling in the Framework, it was found that most of the data collection for individual case studies was completed within about a month. This generally reflected data assembly for historical schemes where it was a case of reconstructing and updating information from old files. For projected schemes more time is obviously necessary to define options, construct working assumptions and assess the economic and environmental consequences afresh. By comparison, it is not unusual for the NCB to spend at least six months on background work before a planning application.

5.2 cont'd

None of these estimates imply full time concentration on one topic but give an indication of the period over which work might extend. Several different disciplines are required to input to the completion of the Framework within NCB itself as well as other affected parties that might be involved in joint working. Recognising the importance of spoil disposal decisions, the scale of work required by the Framework is not felt to be unduly onerous.

- Flexibility

The Framework has considerable flexibility in the circumstances in which it might be applied. For example, options can be defined in terms of different locations, different modes of transport to a particular location, or as different working methods/designs for a particular site. The Framework is most effective when different locations are involved and less sensitive to variations of a particular scheme in broadly the same location.

However, to be used most effectively the Framework must also be operated flexibly. For example, items that are common between different options, such as fines treatment, can be omitted; costs can be included as either overall estimates or calculated from first principles in great detail; the amount of fieldwork conducted in the environmental assessment can be varied; Phase II and most of Phase III can even be by-passed altogether if one option is mutually agreeable to all parties at the end of Phase I. The degree of detail required will depend on the particular circumstances of the scheme and should be something that can be agreed between the NCB and MPA towards the beginning of the exercise.

5.2 cont'd

There was discussion during the testing programme as to whether the Framework should contain a simplified procedure within Phase II for examining straightforward schemes such as some tip extensions. Overall, however, the Consultants felt that to introduce another procedure would merely complicate the Framework and might cause disagreement between the NCB and MPA as to when it was appropriate to use it. The degree of detail included for straightforward schemes can be minimised but it would still be useful to use the existing Framework as a comprehensive checklist to make sure that all issues had been addressed. There may be occasions when the EAC method of summarising costs can be simplified although if a computer routine is being used the calculations are not time consuming and there is sense in all parties familiarising themselves and standardising on one method of reporting.

Another test of flexibility is whether the Framework could be used by other mineral operators if the DoE ultimately recommends its wider use. The conclusion is that the broad philosophy and structure is certainly transferable, although there would need to be some amendment to the individual question-naires to tailor them to different working practices.

- Understandability

There were no problems of comprehension in terms of either the form or overall content of the Framework by the participants in the testing programme. The issues considered in the environmental assessment are, in any case, familiar to NCB Area staff who are now used to operating the checklist procedure designed by the Operational Research Executive. Some Areas have also had exposure to the rigours of analysis at Public Inquiries. The cashflow approach used in the economic appraisal is different from the normal accruals method used by the NCB when reporting results in management accounts but caused no problems of understanding. Assessment of capital investment proposals within the NCB is, however, carried out on a cashflow basis.

5.2 cont'd

Most NCB Area accountancy departments appear to be very familiar with micro-computer technology and no problems are envisaged with the Phase II economic routine. This can in any case still be calculated manually if required.

The Framework is intended to encompass input from a number of different specialists and not all need to be equally familiar with all the techniques required. The Area personnel within the NCB who usually provided information for the case studies were:

Surveyor   -   selection of options and environ-
                            mental assessment

Accountant   -   financial calculations

Civil Engineer   -   initial design of projected schemes
                            and guidelines on unit costs for site
                            preparation, handling and transport

Estates Manager   -   land ownership, restoration and
                            aftercare costs, revenues.

A co-ordinator, who could be one of the above or from ORE or an outside consultant, is also required to translate all the varied data inputs into the Framework.

Certain questions were unclear in early drafts of the Framework but these were clarified during the case studies. The introduction of guidance notes, specific to each part of the Framework, was also found to be helpful by respondents of later case studies.

5.2 cont'd

The only slight problems of comprehension during the case study programme arose when attempting to define options. For many of the historical schemes studied there had genuinely been no realistic options and the attempts of the Study Team on one occasion, artificially to invent options in order to assist the testing of the combined evaluation phase of the Framework, served to cause confusion. This situation should not arise when the Framework is used to assess future schemes, provided that NCB officials have an open mind to evaluating alternatives even if in their professional judgement they already have a preferred solution.

- Clarity

The Framework itself adopts a highly logical approach to building up information and justifying in the final analysis why some issues are considered more important than others.

The NCB may feel that parts of the Framework are too open, particularly the build up of costs. Concern was expressed, during the course of the case study programme, about how the information would be used in practice. The NCB is disinclined to submit the full results of the Framework to MPA officers in confidence in case local authority Members demand that the information is made public and presented in full to Committee meetings. The MPAs have explained that confidential information is provided by other mineral operators and confidence is respected by Members.

An alternative way of proceeding is for the NCB to submit the Phase II summary tables to the MPA formally for use in Committee papers as appropriate, but to show the officers the detailed questionnaires and workings in confidence as background justification to the published results. This would be compatible with the spirit of joint working. The published summary tables would then contain only aggregated data particularly on the costings front so as to safeguard NCB's negotiating position in terms of land purchase and competitive contracts for haulage or other parts of the disposal process.

5.3 Wider Issues

Is Phase III Necessary?

During the design of the Framework it was put to the Consultants by the NCB that the output should take the form of structured summaries of the economic and environmental information without any attempt to combine them. Phase III was therefore, in its eyes, invading the territory of the "decision makers".

There are two main points as to why the Consultants still maintain that Phase III is a valid part of the Framework. The first is that the combined evaluation techniques included do not seek to make the decision on the choice of scheme; they merely try to break the problem down objectively into manageable proportions and try to focus the minds of decision makers on the key trade-offs to be made between a short list of options. The user has the choice of using the decision aiding tools either singly or in combination or not at all, depending on their usefulness in particular circumstances.

Thus Option Rankings is a simple, quick technique which can be presented graphically. Pairwise Comparison is a useful way of breaking down a complex problem and eliminating less good options when there are a large number to be considered. It can lead directly into the Key Issues Statement to focus the main trade-offs to be made by decision makers. Flexibility in use is the key to the operation of the Framework.

The second point concerns who the decision makers are. The formal decision makers in relation to colliery spoil applications will, for the most part, be Local Authority elected members, although in the event of a Public Inquiry, it would be the Secretary of State for the Environment. The NCB has, however, had to go through its own decision making process before submitting its planning application. The Evaluative Framework is primarily designed to help

5.3   cont'd

this process, encouraging liaison with MPA officers at appropriate stages.   To exclude Phase III means that the NCB makes its choice of preferred option on intuitive grounds rather than setting out its reasoning for the MPA and other parties to see.

In respect of the Phase III techniques, it is assumed that the NCB would make some use of these before submitting details to the MPA. Discussions could then be held with the MPA allowing a differing emphasis to be put on the Phase III results where appropriate, before the NCB finally commits itself to a particular option.

It would then be possible for a summary of results from the use of the Evaluative Framework to be submitted to the MPA as background justification to a planning application for a particular option. MPA Members would then have these results available when they made their decision on whether to approve the application or not.   If MPA officers were recommending against the application they might choose to present reworked Phase III tables showing the results of different valuations given to certain factors.

If, as a result of a refusal, the application were reconsidered at a Public Local Inquiry, different interpretations put on the data in the Phase III techniques would form part of each side's evidence.   There may even be additional interpretations given by other interested parties such as MAFF, Water Authorities, environmental pressure and residents' groups who could use the Phase III techniques to express their viewpoints.

How and who uses the Phase III techniques will obviously vary between circumstances but the results of the case study programme give confidence that the suggested techniques can be used flexibly either singly or in combination to assist decision making.

5.3 cont'd

Joint Working in Practice

Another issue raised during the testing programme was how feasible joint working arrangements would be in practice. The Framework envisages that the NCB would play the major role in completing it when there is a need to find a disposal solution for a particular colliery. It would then comprise the major part of the background work necessary before the submission of a planning application. Nevertheless, the MPA would be involved at certain stages during its completion, in particular:

- the identification of options and the selection of which ones to test further;

- the decision on how much detail to include in the testing;

- the provision of some information for the environmental assessment;

- and the sensitivity testing of the combined evaluation results.

Other parties such as MAFF and the Water Authorities would also need to be involved, particularly in the selection of options and in the environmental assessment. Consultation already takes place with these bodies as the NCB is working up a scheme; the Framework merely formalises this involvement.

At the wider level where the Framework might be used to test the viability of transporting spoil to a major reclamation site, it may be that the MPA might take the lead in completing the Framework, involving the NCB particularly in the cost estimates.

5.3   cont'd

The form of working arrangements will no doubt vary between areas, depending on the degree of established liaison between the NCB and MPA. There are not thought to be any problems in principle with the involvement of the MPA as it is not unusual for local authorities to engage in pre-planning application negotiations with developers.

Joint exercises to agree expected spoil arisings and to establish the various time horizons when new tipping arrangements will be required, will often be a forerunner to the use of the Framework.

An extra uncertainty is created by the impending abolition of the Metropolitan Counties which have established liaison arrangements and specialist mineral staff able to understand the operational constraints on the NCB. Similar arrangements do not currently exist with most District Councils in these areas and the principle of joint working may be difficult to establish in the interim. Further, it is unlikely that a District Council could justify the appointment of a full time Minerals Officer with detailed mining knowledge.

The abolition of the Metropolitan Counties will also increase the possibility that, for any given colliery, some of the options chosen may be outside that District's area, thus increasing the number of parties included in the joint working and introducing the possibility of rival interests fragmenting the local authority input.

Is the Framework Really Required?

There was a certain scepticism from some NCB Area officials during the case study programme to the whole concept of the Framework on the grounds that it increases the amount of information demanded in support of a planning application with consequent time penalties on NCB staff. Some questioned whether NCB was being discriminated against when other operators and developers do not have to provide such extensive information.

5.3 cont'd

The NCB corporately though has accepted the usefulness of the Framework procedure, despite the extra effort involved, so that the NCB can be seen to be looking at all disposal options and justifying its preferred choice. It accepts that environmental consciousness is increasing amongst the general public and particularly within certain pressure groups, and believes that the Board should be taking a responsible attitude as an example to other mineral operators.

The NCB suspects that, in the majority of cases, the Framework will identify a local tipping site as the preferred option, and that the environmental advantages of remote options will rarely be sufficient to justify the huge expenditure necessary on transport. All parties hope that the use of the Framework will enable such issues to be thoroughly debated before the submission of a planning application thus avoiding, where possible, the substantial amount of time and costs expended at a Public Inquiry.

Part 2
Review of Existing Procedures

TECHNICAL REVIEW

6.0 SPOIL PRODUCTION

6.1 Sources and Quantities of Spoil

Generally spoil is the waste material that is extracted in the process of mining deep coal. Coal is won at the face by machine and in doing so the dirt bands (which are interspersed with coal seams), seat-earths and parts of the seam roof are also extracted. With intensive mechanised methods it is judged to be efficient to raise the dirt mixed with the coal to the surface. This mixture is known as run-of-mine and, at the surface, the coal has to be extracted to become a marketable product.

In the past, mining methods produced relatively little waste above ground as coal excavation by hand was highly selective and most waste was separated and left underground.

National estimates of the quantities of spoil produced by the different aspects of the mining process are given in Table 6.1 for 1979/80 (Ref.8). These proportions will vary slightly between years depending on the amount of new mine construction work.

TABLE 6.1

SOURCES AND QUANTITIES OF SPOIL PRODUCED IN 1979/80

Source of Dirt	Quantity in million tonnes
Coal face - roof, seam, floor etc.	35
- face rippings	10
Development Drivages	10
Roadway Repairs	6
Ad hoc sources	6
TOTAL	67

Source : Blelloch (Ref.8)

Not all of this spoil results in a waste product for disposal on the surface, as in excess of 15% (some 11 million tonnes) is either left underground or left in the saleable coal.

6.1 cont'd

Underground retention of spoil normally comprises only the limited activity of constructing gateside packs, associated with the long-wall advancing method of mining, from the larger sizes of discard created in driving roadways. The packs are stacked around the roadway behind supports and often strengthened. Some gateside packing is done by low pressure stowage methods.

Storage of waste in the void created behind the coal face was common in the UK in the 1930s when labour for the construction of the packs was relatively cheap. As coal cutting became more capital intensive, experiments were undertaken with mechanical stowing, particularly pneumatic, although this generally required spoil to be wound to the surface, prepared and then returned underground.

Several experiments in stowing waste took place in the 1950s, particularly at collieries in South Wales but, as mechanised coal cutting became more efficient in the 1960s, such systems were found to be unnecessary. The last known application was between 1975 and 1981 at Park Mill Colliery in West Yorkshire (Ref.9). Here, careful cutting enabled the upper and lower coal seams to be transported to the surface and the thick middle dirt band to be retained underground and stowed, using low pressure equipment, along a 40 metre section of the face. This practice stopped when the particular seam was worked out and no other applications are known to be taking place now in the UK.

Power stations currently accept between 13 and 18% spoil (termed ash content) in coal supplied for coal fired boilers. In some limited cases, where coal seams are relatively clean, this means that run-of-mine can be transported straight to power stations, after sizing and crushing, with no need for further cleaning and therefore spoil disposal. This is expected to happen for example at the new Selby mines. In other cases, for example at the Longannet complex in Scotland, run-of-mine coal contains too high an ash content and requires higher grade coals to be added as a "sweetener" before use in the adjacent power station. These higher grade coals often come from opencast sites. The majority of coal used in power stations has, however, been through the washing and screening process in the coal preparation plant (CPP) in order to separate out excess spoil.

This Research Project is largely concerned with the waste element, known as spoil, that is produced on the surface when coal is extracted from the run-of-mine material in the CPP. For the purposes of the Project the "production" or starting point for spoil generation is taken to be this output from the CPP. No account is taken here of methods that could be used to reduce spoil make.

The introduction of modern mechanised techniques in the UK coal industry and the gradual lowering of acceptable ash content by CEGB has greatly increased the proportion of spoil arising from deep coal mining operations. The scale of the NCB's problem is illustrated in Figure 6.1 which shows the increase in the amount of

G

**Annual saleable coal output
and waste deposited on land**

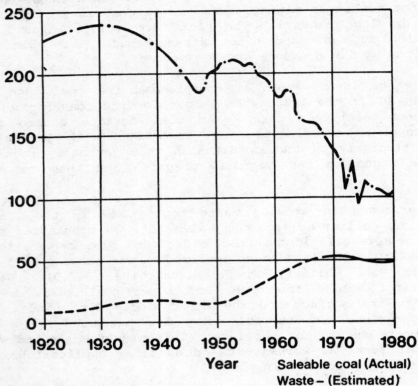

Millions of Tons

Saleable coal (Actual)
Waste – (Estimated)
        (Actual)

**Percentages of saleable coal
mechanically cleaned and power loaded**

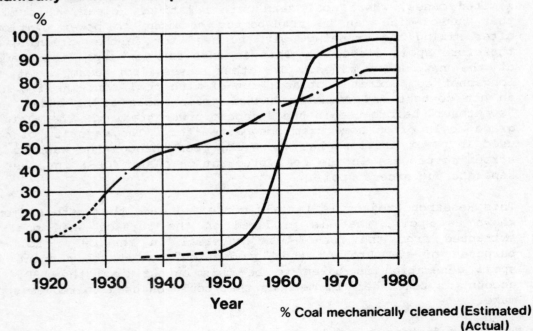

% Coal mechanically cleaned (Estimated)
                            (Actual)
% Coal power loaded (Estimated)
                    (Actual)

Source: Reproduced from Ref.1

**COAL AND WASTE
PRODUCTION 1920-1980**

FIGURE 6·1

6.1 cont'd

colliery spoil produced compared with saleable coal, particularly
since the 1950s and 1960s. In addition, the production of spoil
has become increasingly concentrated in such areas as the central
coalfield.

The national output of spoil production is currently at a rate of
55% of saleable output, a ratio of about 1:2. The NCB maintains
that this has now stabilised in national terms. This means that if
future coal production falls, so should the volume of spoil.
However, increasing localisation of spoil production is expected to
be a continuing trend as more and more of the nation's coal is
produced in the modern coalfields with the greatest reserves
(particularly the Yorks, Notts, Derby coalfield), and as more
output from individual collieries is brought to the surface at a
single complex in local concentration schemes.

The proportion of spoil to coal varies considerably in different
parts of the country, ranging from 29% in the NCB South Midlands
Area to 79% in South Nottinghamshire (see Table 6.2). The location
of the NCB Areas is shown in Figure 6.2 with those in the Yorks,
Notts, Derby coalfield highlighted. During 1985 two sets of Areas
have been combined: North Yorkshire and Barnsley, and Doncaster and
South Yorkshire. All tables in this report are based on the pre
1985 Area structure.

TABLE 6.2

SPOIL DISPOSED COMPARED TO COAL OUTPUT
IN 1981/82 BY NCB AREA

	Spoil Disposed (million tonnes)	Saleable Output (million tonnes)	Spoil Disposed as % of Saleable Output
Yorks/Notts/Derby Coalfield			
North Yorkshire	6.0	8.3	72
Doncaster	3.3	7.1	46
Barnsley	5.4	8.4	64
South Yorkshire	5.0	7.2	69
North Nottinghamshire	7.0	12.2	60
South Nottinghamshire	6.8	8.6	79
North Derbyshire	4.0	8.5	47
Rest of UK			
Scotland	2.3	7.2	32
North East	6.4	13.4	48
South Midlands	2.5	8.6	29
Western	4.5	11.0	41
South Wales	5.7	7.5	76
TOTAL	58.9	108.0	55

Note: Includes marine disposal
Based on pre 1985 Area Structure

Source : Butler and Dunn (Ref. 7)

6.1 cont'd

There are three main factors which influence the spoil/coal ratio:-

-   geology
    (where thick coal seams are being worked it is often possible
    to construct the underground service roadways within the seam
    thus minimising the production of spoil. Thinner seams
    require roof or floor strata to be worked in forming the
    roadways. Inevitably, any inherent dirt within the seam must
    be extracted with the coal);

-   method of mining
    (the "advance" method requires underground service roadways to
    be constructed as the face moves forward. The sides of these
    roadways are supported by "packs" built with stone or dirt
    thereby reducing the amount of dirt brought to the surface.
    In "retreat" mining the roadways are constructed initially and
    any dirt encountered must be brought out with the development
    coal);

-   markets
    (coal produced for industry and the coking market needs to
    have a lower ash content than that supplied to power stations.
    Levels acceptable to the latter market have changed over
    time).

The relative proportions of spoil to coal produced vary not only at
coalfield level and individual colliery level, but also over time
at any particular location, as variations in geological conditions
are encountered or as markets change.

Nationally, spoil disposed of amounted to nearly 59 million tonnes
(1981/82) (Table 6.2) about two-thirds of which was tipped in the
Yorks, Notts, Derby coalfield. This compares with about 10 million
tonnes of pulverised fuel ash and 22 million tonnes of china clay
waste tipped nationally (Ref.10). Solid refuse in England and
Wales was about 28 million tonnes in 1984/85, only 13% of which was
produced in the Yorks, Notts, Derby area (Ref.11).

The NCB is not aware of any research or anticipated changes in
mining practice which could lead to significantly less spoil being
mined in the short term. There are some projects in hand which
could lead to minor reductions, such as more instant and accurate
control of the face cutting machine with the use of nucleonic
sensing attachments. Small variations in the position of the
cutting tool at the face can have considerable effects on the make
of spoil. Improvements are also being made to systems which give
advance warning of in-situ faults ahead of the coal face. Overall
though, the current orders of magnitude of spoil produced
nationally are expected to continue into the future.

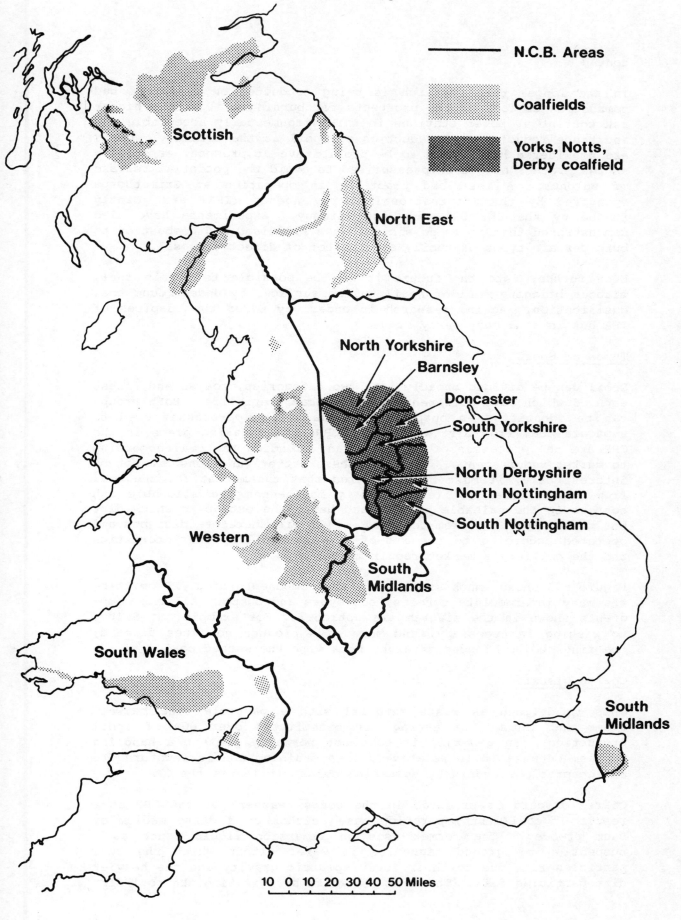

N.C.B. Areas

Coalfields

Yorks, Notts, Derby coalfield

Scottish

North East

North Yorkshire

Barnsley

Doncaster

South Yorkshire

North Derbyshire

North Nottingham

South Nottingham

Western

South Midlands

South Wales

South Midlands

10 0 10 20 30 40 50 Miles

Source: NCB

YORKS, NOTTS, DERBY COALFIELD AND N.C.B. AREAS (as at January 1985)

FIGURE 6·2

6.1   cont'd

In the longer term research is being conducted on fluidised bed
combustion to look at the prospects for burning coal with a higher
ash content at power stations in an environmentally acceptable way
and hence reducing the production of spoil at the colliery. Costs
are considered by the NCB to be prohibitive at present, especially
as the process has to be pressurised to avoid the potential release
of sulphur.   A test bed plant is in operation at Grimethorpe
sponsored by the International Energy Agency (IEA) and jointly
funded by the UK, USA and West Germany. Experiments have also
demonstrated that it is possible to use fluidised bed combustion to
burn certain types of spoil, as a method of direct disposal.

Even further into the future it may be possible to obtain fuel,
without bringing coal or spoil to the surface, by underground coal
gasification. Again, research is under way under the auspices of
IEA but is at a very early stage.

6.2   Types of Spoil

Spoil can be divided broadly into two categories, coarse and fines,
each of which have different disposal characteristics. Both groups
can be identified as outputs from the various processes used to
separate coal from dirt within the CPP. Also taking place in the
CPP are the processes of screening and blending the coal according
to market requirements. Although these latter functions are not of
interest here, it must be remembered that the market for the coal
from a particular colliery directly influences the allowable ash
content in the saleable product and hence the extent to which dirt
has to be separated from the coal. CPPs are therefore designed and
operated according to the run-of-mine washability characteristics
and the colliery's market requirements.

Figure 6.3 shows, much simplified, the components of a CPP omitting
the many intermediate screens, conveyors and pumps. All the components shown in the diagram are optional. For example, at Selby,
no washing is necessary, and some pits produce no fines discard;
the fines being blended straight back with the washed coal.

Coarse Discard

This is defined as waste material with a particle size between
0.5mm and 150mm. On average it constitutes over 80% of spoil
production. In general, it does not normally present a handling
problem because it is relatively free draining and is dewatered to
an acceptable standard by screening before it leaves the CPP.

Coarse discard is produced in the coarse washery of the CPP as a
result of coal/dirt separation based either on a dense medium or
Baum process. The former uses an immersion liquid, such as a
suspension of ground magnetite in water within which the coal
particles rise due to their lower specific gravity and the heavier
dirt particles fall. The Baum jig works by agitating the coal/dirt

Coal prep. plant.

6.2   cont'd

mixture in water, thus inducing separation. Comparing the two processes, Baum jigs require a more consistent feed and do not give as efficient a cut off point between coal and shale as in the dense medium process; they are however, cheaper to operate. There is no appreciable difference in the characteristics of coarse discard produced by either process.

The typical moisture content of fresh coarse discard as it leaves the CPP is about 10%.

Fines Discard

This material has a nominal maximum particle size of 0.5mm although a large proportion can be of much smaller size being less than 10 microns. It can constitute up to 20% of spoil production. Because of the particle size distribution the material is not free draining and therefore presents greater handling and disposal problems than coarse discard. It generally consists of fine clay and shale particles.

Fines discard is produced in the fines washery of the CPP at the end of the froth flotation process. This process separates the fine coal and fine dirt by adding oil and a frothing agent to the coal/dirt suspension in a conditioner. The fine coal rises to the surface because the air bubbles attach themselves to the coal particles and cause them to float. This procedure is, however, not used in all CPPs. In some plants, where the fines mixture has a high spoil content, fine coal extraction may not be economic and all fines produced from the washery are treated as discard. In other plants, where the ash content is low, the whole of the fines may be dewatered by a combination of a settling tank, slurry cyclone and filter to produce a filter cake which can be blended back with the larger coal and sold.

Where a froth flotation process is used, the fines discard sinks to the bottom and is referred to as tailings. This discard is very dilute and is further treated with a flocculent which causes the particles to settle in a thickener, leaving clear water overflowing the rim of the thickener tank for re-use within the CPP. At this stage the thickened tailings resemble a sludge with a moisture content of between 60 and 70%.

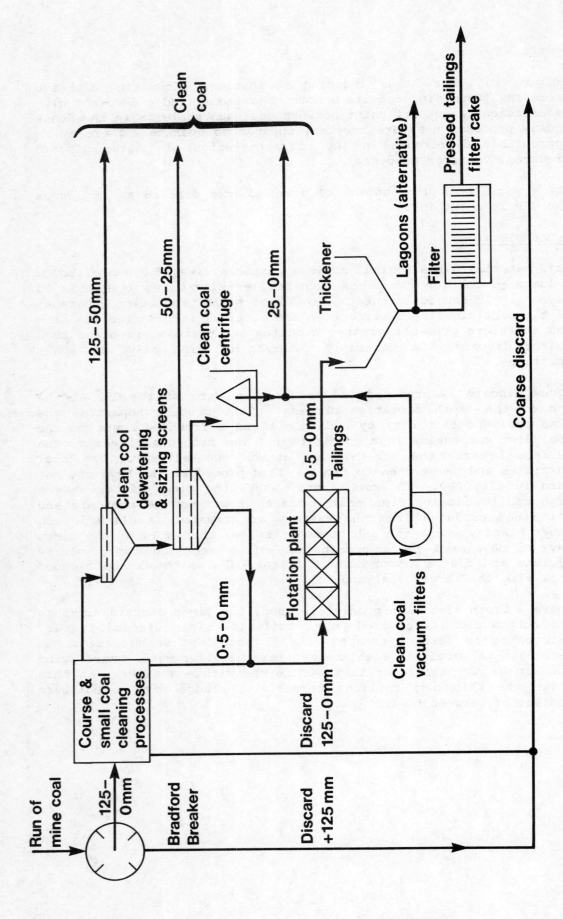

Source: NCB

**A TYPICAL
COAL PREPARATION PLANT**

FIGURE 6·3

6.2 cont'd

The tailings sludge can then either be disposed of by liquid discharge to lagoons or be further dewatered by various forms of mechanical equipment. The products can be classified into three broad groups with varying moisture content (m_c).

    i]   Suspensions   -   sufficiently fluid to be pumped
          ($m_c > 50\%$)   readily to an impoundment i.e. lagoon.

    ii]   Semi-solid   -   too solid to be pumped but too
          ($25\% < m_c < 50\%$)   wet to be placed on the tip without further treatment unless impounded.

    iii]   Solid   -   sufficiently solid to be handled
          ($m_c < 25\%$)   and transported in the same way as coarse discard. The solid is known either as pressed or filtercake.

Examples of dewatering equipment which produce a semi-solid product are deep cone thickeners and rotary vacuum filters. These were relatively early developments and generally require the addition of either cement or lime before the output can be disposed. The NCB is not considering the further use or extension of either of these processes at new collieries on both reliability and cost grounds.

Developments currently at the testing stage which still produce a semi-solid product are refinements of the solid bowl centrifuge (36-42% m_c) and the multi-roller filter belt press (38-43% m_c). Both these operate as continuous processes thus reducing manpower requirements, but they may still require cement stabilisation before tipping. The multi-roller filter belt press has been used for a number of years in the paper industry and for sewage treatment.

The most common type of dewatering equipment which produces a solid product (20-25% m_c) is the conventional filter press. The membrane filter press is a development of this which produces an output within the range 18-22%. These two methods are the only proven techniques of producing a pressed cake for disposal on a tip without further treatment. Filter presses are batch processes and are labour intensive.

The earliest filter presses were installed by the NCB in 1951 and were 0.84m x 0.84m x 40 chamber recessed plate filter presses. These had an output of 3 tonnes/hour. These presses were found to be relatively unreliable and very labour intensive (because filter cakes had to be manually discharged), and inappropriate in dealing with larger requirements for tailings treatment (Ref.12). To meet this demand the NCB has installed many more larger and reliable presses (2m x 1.5m x 100 chambers up to 2m x 2m x 150 chambers) capable of dealing with from 10 to 20 tonnes of dry material per cycle (equivalent to 1 to 2 hours pressing time).

6.2   cont'd

Over 100 filter presses were said to be in operation within the NCB
in 1979 and another 70 to 80 were being installed (Ref.12).   The
move towards filter presses was in line with trends in Germany and
the United States.   Modern types of filter presses are used in the
new CPPs at the large concentration schemes in the NCB Barnsley
Area.   Grimethorpe Colliery currently has the largest filter press
plant in the country with 24 presses.

However, increasing the efficiency of the new presses depends on:

   i]   uniform filtrate and continuous supply,

   ii]   more automatic control to reduce manpower levels,

   iii]   effective washing of the filter cloths at optimum inter-
          vals,

   iv]   matching cycle-time to desired moisture content.

The membrane plate press is a development of the conventional
filter press which allows it to operate with a variable volume or
cake thickness.   With a conventional filter press of fixed volume
it is necessary to fill the recesses and to continue pumping until
sufficient solids have been introduced to produce a cake of the
required moisture content.   A membrane plate press enables greater
control on cake thickness (independently of the moisture content)
and therefore advantage can be taken of the reduced pressing time
to give a higher rate of output, particularly with tailings that
are difficult to dewater.   The output can approach double that of a
conventional filter press.

The drawback is that thinner cakes require more frequent discharges
and unless cakes can be made to release and drop easily these
presses can become very labour intensive.   The presses are also
slightly more expensive than the conventional filter presses in
capital terms.

By 1983 the NCB had installed a total of nine membrane filter
presses at Hucknall and Parkside Collieries but these have so far
met with mixed success.   Further testing of automatic presses with
full cloth cleaning facilities will take place when the NCB is
satisfied that such systems are reliable. Manufacturers claim that
such systems only require a single person supervision during
discharge (10 minutes during a 1½ to 2 hour cycle time);   NCB
disputes this.

Membrane plate filter presses have been used extensively in other
industries enabling a higher throughput because of reduced cycle
times.

6.2 cont'd

The one factor that has eluded all the developers and manufacturers of filter presses is the problem of cake release, i.e. removing all the material from the moulds. The benefits obtained from an unmanned operation are obvious and the NCB is currently assessing a fully automatic press marketed in Europe from Denmark and known as the Lasta press. High capital costs are involved but presses have a higher capacity for a given size compared to conventional presses. Fully automatic presses have been in use for over a decade in the chemical and sewage treatment industries.

6.3 Proportion of Fines Discard

Coupled with the general increase in spoil production has been a steady increase in the proportion of fines within the spoil.

This increase in fines, which is a pattern occurring throughout the world, can be attributed in the UK to:-

- the progressive introduction of power loading at the coal face;

- the use of dust suppression techniques underground (which may degrade the spoil);

- the mechanisation of cutting development dirt, most of which now goes through the CPP against the previous method of bringing it out separately;

- the working of thinner seams and the increasing proportion of shales as mining has moved eastwards in the central coalfield;

- the proportion of coal which is mechanically cleaned (these being wet processes).

Coal preparation plants (CPPs) were designed in the 1950s to cope with up to 10% fines within raw coal but are now designed for about 20% fines. After processing in the CPP this fines proportion generally yields about 60% fines coal and 40% tailings (fines discard).

In 1950 fines discard comprised in the order of 3% of total discard nationally; in 1960 this had risen to 8%; by 1970 12% and by 1980 12.5% but it can range up to 20% at certain collieries.

6.4 Commercial Utilisation

The amount of spoil requiring disposal each year is further reduced by a small amount being sold commercially straight from the CPP. This only amounts to about 0.5 million tonnes of the total 5 to 10 million tonnes per annum used commercially, (Ref.10). Spoil taken from existing heaps rather than fresh-wrought spoil from the CPP is usually preferred as it is drier, and quality and quantity can more easily be controlled.

6.4 cont'd

There are several potential uses for colliery spoil in engineering and construction fields, and it is the role of the Minestone Executive within the NCB to develop these markets. However, spoil is in competition with many other sources of waste product as well as natural aggregates and it has generally only been competitive to use it when a demand arises close to a colliery.

Table 6.3 shows the uses to which spoil was put in 1976. The most significant use was as a bulk fill material in civil engineering works, mainly road construction. The two other major markets are for use in cement stabilised working areas and for use in reinforced earth retaining structures.

TABLE 6.3

SPOIL UTILISED COMMERCIALLY IN 1976

Use	Source of Spoil ('000 tonnes)	
	From current coal production	From existing heaps
Fill	225	5500
Brickmaking	150	400
Cement Works	65	65
Light Aggregates for concrete	-	1000
TOTAL	500	7005

Source : CENE (Ref.1) Table 9.3

Further details of the different types of utilisation for colliery spoil are given in Appendix E.

7.0   DISPOSAL METHODS

7.1   Quantities

Not all the 67 million tonnes of spoil generated nationally
(1979/80) requires disposal because, as already seen, a certain
proportion is retained underground, is left in the coal sold to
power stations and used by industry, or is sold commercially. The
remaining 56 or so million tonnes requires disposal as a waste
product. Disposal represents the activities of handling, transport
and placement (Restoration is dealt with in the next chapter).
Disposal locations are predominantly land-based, on farmland or in
existing voids close to the originating colliery. About 5 million
tonnes of spoil in North East England is subject to marine
disposal.

The official recording of spoil laid to ground by the NCB on a
nationally consistent basis is made by means of the Annual Tip
Review produced on an Area basis generally by means of photo-
grammetry. The first year in which the Annual Tip Review was
co-ordinated at national level was 1982. The production of results
from succeeding surveys has been interrupted by the recent industrial action and are not yet available.

Land-based tipping accounts for over 90% (51 million tonnes) of the
total annual disposal of dirt nationally. Except in the NCB North
East Area it is the only method used. Most of this is tipped on
spoil heaps but, at the time of the CENE Report (1981) (Ref.1),
about 4 million tonnes was used in local land reclamation projects,
for example filling old mineral working voids or raising the level
of low-lying low quality agricultural land. The remaining 47
million tonnes or so is tipped on conventional spoil tips including
lagoons.

The split between lagooning and dry tipping is currently not available but should be identified in the 1983 Annual Tip Review. The
NCB estimates that fines represent about 12½% of total discard in
the Yorks, Notts, Derby coalfield, of which about two-thirds is
pumped to lagoons. Applying these proportions to the national
figures suggest a split between conventional tips and lagoons of
about 43 to 4 million tonnes respectively. Other methods of
treating fines, such as the output of filter presses and deep cone
thickeners, produces a discard with a lower moisture content which
can be disposed of on conventional tips.

The main disposal methods are considered in turn below. A more
detailed description of disposal methods in the Yorks, Notts, Derby
coalfield is included at Appendix F.

7.2   Surface Tipping

The majority of surface tipping comprises the construction of spoil
heaps immediately adjacent to the particular colliery. Spoil tips
can be constructed of either coarse discard or a mixture of coarse
discard and dewatered treated fines.

7.2   cont'd

The disposal of dry discard is essentially a mechanical handling problem. The sustained rate of spoil production from the CPP averages about 60-70 tonnes per hour at UK collieries. At this level most stages in the tipping process can be handled by mobile earth moving equipment. Only at large colliery complexes, such as Grimethorpe with spoil output in the order of 600 tonnes per hour, does substantial investment in specialised plant become justified.

Because the material is free draining due to its large particle size the construction of coarse discard tips is a relatively straightforward operation, given normal weather conditions. An important physical property of spoil, which affects its handling, is the bulk density of coarse discard at various stages of the disposal process. Depending on site location the compacted bulk density of tipped material will range between 1.8 and 2.2 tonnes per cubic metre. The bulk density of loose spoil, which will be of significance during transport, depends on the method of measurement and varies between 1.0 and 1.5 tonnes per cubic metre. An average estimate of placed spoil can be taken as between 1.75 and 1.9 tonnes per cubic metre.

Handling of dewatered fines in the form of semi-solids (after further drying by impoundment or mixing with cement) or solids is more difficult because the small grain size retains water and reduces the material's shear strength. There are two ways of constructing tips made from treated fines (pressed cake) and coarse discard and these are illustrated in Figure 7.1.

Method A involves mixing the two materials at the CPP where it is then transported either by conveyor or dump truck to the tip. Method B involves transporting the materials separately to the tip where the pressed cake is laid and then capped by a layer of coarse discard. The latter method is normally favoured by the NCB because of its better drainage characteristics and easier handling although marginally more land is active at any one time.

The design of tips has changed over the years from the traditional conical tips of uncompacted spoil placed by cable ways or Maclane tippers to generally lower tips with flatter side slopes. The design of tipping is controlled by two documents. The NCB (Production) Codes and Rules : Tips, 1971 is the NCB's internal rule book for the design and operation of tips and is primarily a working document covering the implementation of the Mines and Quarries (Tips) Regulations 1971. This document specifies the various inspections and reports which must be produced for proposed, existing and disused tips. Complementary with this document is the Technical Handbook : Spoil Heaps and Lagoons, which is a detailed manual of tip and lagoon design and operation, almost wholly concerned with safety. The latter document is currently being redrafted.

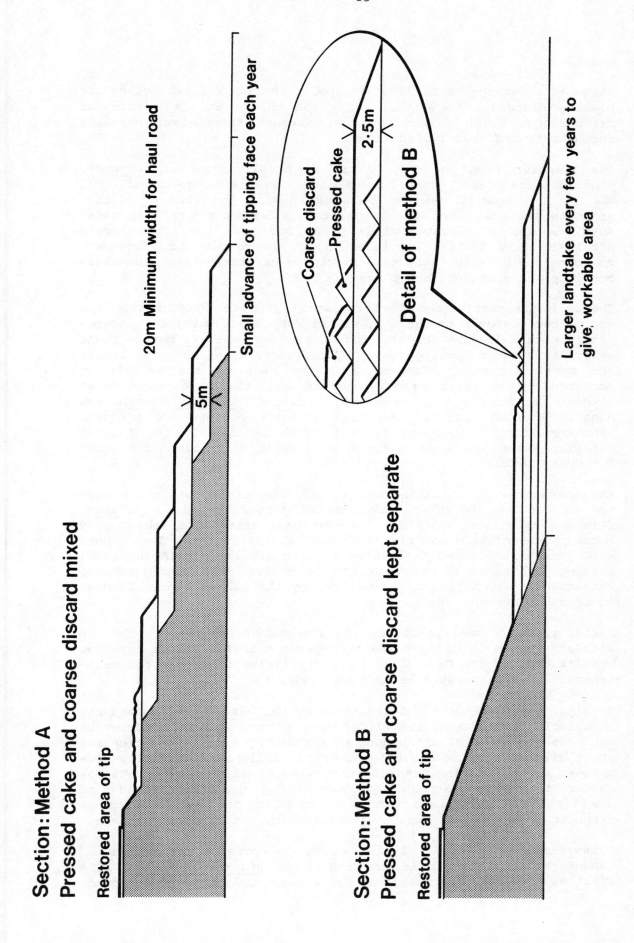

Section: Method A
Pressed cake and coarse discard mixed

Restored area of tip

20m Minimum width for haul road

Small advance of tipping face each year

5m

Section: Method B
Pressed cake and coarse discard kept separate

Restored area of tip

Coarse discard

Pressed cake

2·5m

Detail of method B

Larger landtake every few years to give workable area

Source: Reproduced from Ref. 13

METHODS OF TIP CONSTRUCTION

FIGURE 7·1

7.2 cont'd

There is an extensive range of equipment available for handling and placing discard onto a local tip, the choice in any particular circumstance being dependent upon distance thresholds, capacity throughputs and cost implications.

The transfer from the CPP to tip is usually done by <u>conveyor</u>. Conveyors are ideally suited for medium distance movements of spoil and do not usually need to be moved during the life of a tip, although they may need to be extended. Conveyors are less noisy than the use of surface mobile plant and have low labour costs after the high initial capital outlay. In respect of placement, the conveyor usually feeds to a stockpile or dirt bunker from where mobile plant transport and place the spoil.

The main alternative means of transport from the CPP or from the end of the conveyor to the tip, is the dump truck working in assoc- iation with a loading shovel. Off-highway <u>dump trucks</u> may be rigid or articulated for poor ground. NCB use capacities up to 55 tonnes for spoil disposal. Tipping from the rear of the vehicle is actuated by hydraulic rams. Labour and fuel are major cost elements as with all surface mobile plant. <u>Loading shovels</u> are usually wheeled loaders with high capacity buckets and adequate tractive effort for loose material such as spoil. The largest capacity shovel operated by the NCB on spoil disposal is currently 5.5 cubic metres.

An alternative to a loading shovel and dump truck, which combines the two actions together with that of compaction, is a <u>scraper</u>. This can be effective up to a one-way haul distance of about 1500 metres. Essentially motorised scrapers are articulated dump trucks with hydraulic powered facilities to give digging action when bowl loading and material ejection in the bottom dump configuration. The largest capacity scraper operated by the NCB on spoil disposal is 18 cubic metres.

Aerial ropeways used to be used as a means of transfer to the tip with advantages in hilly terrain. Most old installations have now been removed in the UK. They cause difficulty of access for main- tenance and are susceptible to high winds.

An alternative method of placement is by <u>bulldozer</u>. Bulldozers are invariably tracked vehicles fitted with a front mounted blade which can excavate material and propel it forward by a rolling action for short distances up to about 100 metres. Bulldozers generally have a lower ground bearing pressure than wheeled earth-moving vehicles and are therefore safer working close to the unconsolidated edge of new tipping. Bulldozers can also work in conjunction with an extending conveyor, eliminating the need for intermediate haulage.

A new concept for spoil tipping which incorporates the actions of transfer and placement is the radial or <u>stacker spreader</u>. The first experimental machine is at Grimethorpe Colliery and a second

7.2   cont'd

is being installed at South Kirkby Colliery, both in Barnsley Area. The discard is transported along a trunk conveyor and is then transferred to a face conveyor at right angles to it. This second belt is capable of being slewed as the face develops. Spoil is then transferred to the radial spreader. Both the transfer unit between the link conveyors and the spreader itself are mounted on crawlers to give mobility and low ground pressure. The method of operation requires an initial embankment to be prepared by conventional means prior to laying out the face belt. The radial spreader then works from this level either side of the face belt to advance the leading edge in 6 metre layers. These layers are spread by bulldozer, which has a higher ground pressure than the spreader, thus ensuring that there are no voids and no risk to the stability of the spreader. The spreader then works on the trailing side of the face belt to form three successive 6 metre lifts to achieve the final profile of the tip. The main advantages of the machine are claimed to be reduced operating noise and financial benefits due to reduced surface mobile plant requirements. The capital costs are in the order of £1 million, and therefore such machines are only viable at high throughput sites.

Compaction equipment is not generally used in the construction of spoil tips as the action of spreading spoil in thin layers and the passage of haulage and placement plant ensures sufficient compaction of spoil and the exclusion of air voids.

Other processes associated with tipping operations largely utilise items of the above equipment. Site preparation, including any demolition and tree removal, will use a bulldozer, while soil stripping and replacement will use a scraper. The maintenance of haul roads will use a motor grader or, on smaller sites, perhaps a bulldozer.

7.3   Lagoons

When lagoons are incorporated in tips the two types of discard, coarse and fines (ie tailings), are handled separately. The coarse discard is used to construct the banks and the tailings are pumped in suspension to the impoundment formed by the banks where the particles are allowed to settle. The supernatant water is drawn off, usually for return to the CPP. When the lagoon is filled and the tailings have dried out sufficiently to support the weight of tracked vehicles, the lagoon can be overtipped with coarse discard as a prelude to restoration.

The land requirement of a lagoon depends on its size. Many lagoons are between 1 and 2 hectares but can be much bigger, for example the former lagoon within the Gedling Colliery coarse tip is 11 hectares. Normally, the use of lagoons has to be phased, with usually at least two or three being required at any one time, one being built, one being filled and one drying out, to allow the site to be developed progressively. At Woolley Colliery, however, there are 12 lagoons although overtipping is in progress or planned on 8 of these.

H

7.3   cont'd

Lagoons are only a practicable proposition when the topography is gentle and where slopes do not exceed 1:12. Where steep land slopes exist, the volume of bank material required to contain the lagoon is large compared with the contained tailings volume unless a whole valley feature could be dammed. Lagoon areas are usually close to the colliery to reduce pipeline and pumping costs. Lagoons are now rarely found at high levels within tips. All tipping is strictly controlled according to the NCB Codes and Rules, Tips 1971.

Tailings are pumped to lagoons in suspension in water. Hydraulic pipelines are a relatively cheap means of transport compared with road and rail charges for dry spoil and are generally not intrusive environmentally. There are several examples where the NCB has disposed of wet fines off-site, pumping the material into old quarries or sand and gravel pits; lagoons can also be created in opencast voids. This has the advantage of reclaiming land back to agricultural use and taking the pressure off limited tipping land closer to the colliery. Wet fines can also be transported off-site by road or rail tanker.

The total number of settling lagoons in the Yorks, Notts, Derby coalfield was estimated at 225 at the time of CENE (1980). No information has been made available during the Project to update this position.

In 1982, CENE (Ref.1) recommended to the Government that lagoons should be avoided wherever possible and that new mines should be designed to prevent the discharge of untreated tailings. This recommendation was based on the perceived environmental impacts of lagoons, namely:-

-   land take

-   delay to restoration

-   visual intrusion from high viewpoints

-   safety hazard particularly to children (para. 9.21).

These recommendations were accepted by the NCB and welcomed by the MPAs. However, MPAs claim that in recent years the NCB has been increasing its dependence on lagoons rather than reducing it, even where equipment exists at collieries for processing the tailings.

7.4   Backfilling of Voids

In some cases it is possible to use spoil to backfill voids that have either been left unrestored by previous mineral operators or

7.4 cont'd

are currently being created. From the environmental point of view
such schemes can have the following advantages:

-    returning derelict or degraded land to a positive after-use
     which might otherwise be delayed or never carried out because
     of a shortage of materials for restoration;

-    preventing the sterilisation of other mineral sources and the
     possible creation of unrestored land if extraction and back-
     filling with spoil can be planned and executed together;

-    diverting or delaying pressures for the use of other land for
     spoil disposal, particularly land of good agricultural quality
     or of special landscape value, or sometimes a combination of
     both.

The constraint on the widescale use of this disposal method is the
cost of transport unless suitable voids can be found in close
proximity to a colliery.

Of the different types of mineral voids, hard rock quarries usually
have the greatest capacity because they tend to have deep, steep
sides. If operations are taking place concurrently, timescales are
usually sufficiently long to permit gradual backfilling to occur at
the same time as new areas of the site are opened up. Use of
limestone quarries or chalk pits will usually require special
protective measures to ensure that there is no pollution of ground
water.

Sand and gravel or clay pits are relatively shallow and require a
large surface area to provide sufficient capacity for several years
output of spoil from average sized collieries. Special precautions
may need to be taken against seepage and/or scour if pits are
located in river valleys.

The capacity of voids created through opencast mining is usually
rather limited, because the coal is carefully extracted, little if
any spoil is produced and the bulking of the overburden and
sub-soil may lead to an increase in volume. However, opportunities
to create a new landform with extra capacity for spoil disposal are
sometimes possible.

The dual use of the site by Opencast Executive and Deep Mines
requires careful phasing of the different operations. The filling
of the void can either be carried out after all opencast activity
has been completed, or progressive backfilling can take place
simultaneously behind the opencast works. The different methods of
joint working will depend upon the characteristics of the site and
the availability of space around the site to accommodate the overburden and soil. The timescale of opencast mining is much shorter
than hard rock quarrying.

There are opportunities for the co-disposal of refuse and colliery
spoil into existing voids. Colliery spoil is a relatively good

7.4 cont'd

cover material for refuse and can also be used to create a landform with suitable hidden voids for refuse, as proposed in the Welbeck scheme in West Yorkshire. The two waste products can also be tipped together into old quarries or into opencast sites, as at the Erin site in Derbyshire, although this requires strict operational controls.

There are also opportunities for co-disposal of pfa and colliery spoil. Colliery spoil can be used as the material for constructing bund walls for the impoundment of pfa slurry, as in the Gale Common scheme in North Yorkshire. Colliery spoil can also be used as a capping material over pfa to give a better draining surface for agricultural restoration, as was suggested in the Peterborough (Fletton) option as a possible remote disposal location for spoil from the North East Leicestershire Coalfield.

However, major concentrations of solid refuse, pfa and colliery spoil outputs in a given area may put pressure on the availability of suitable tipping sites and voids. There does not appear to be much direct competition at the moment between pfa and colliery spoil for the identification of new sites. This is mainly because the CEGB currently has a large amount of permitted capacity because of its policy of identifying at least 15 years tipping capacity, usually with potential for expansion, at the time of commissioning power stations. It may be that some sites that might have been suitable for future colliery spoil disposal have already been ear-marked for pfa. For example, if fines lagooning in old sand and gravel pits is successful in South Nottinghamshire and is to be repeated, there might be competition as the CEGB already has permission for pfa disposal in many of the Trent Valley gravel pits.

There is potentially more competition between solid refuse and colliery spoil for limited void space. For example, available quarries in Tyne and Wear have been designated for solid refuse disposal leaving few, if any, land-based options as an alternative to current sea dumping of spoil from coastal collieries.

7.5 Marine Disposal

Marine disposal is largely restricted to the NCB's North East Area where it has traditionally been used as a form of local tipping for coastal collieries. Small quantities are also involved in Scotland and until recently in Lancashire (Ref.1).

In the North East sea tipping from barges accounts for about 1.6 million tonnes of coarse discard per annum, currently from three coastal collieries: Bates, Westoe and Wearmouth. Licences are granted to the NCB by MAFF and Department of Trade and the material is tipped in defined disposal points between 8 and 16 kilometres off-shore. Concerns have been expressed about the effects of this practice on habitats and fisheries. The Government, in its White Paper, "Coal and the Environment" (Ref.2), accepts CENE's recommendation that sea tipping is not an option to pursue for the future.

7.5   cont'd

Beach tipping is currently occurring at a rate of about 3.2 million
tonnes a year, under appropriate licences from MAFF, Crown Estate
Commissioners and Department of Trade. It is centred on four
coastal collieries: Lynemouth, Vane Tempest/Dawdon, Easington and
Horden. The first two collect spoil from three other inland
collieries. Beach tipping at a fifth site, Blackhall, stopped in
1975 and the beach has been restored by Durham County Council using
Derelict Land Grant (DLG) monies. Such tipping has been a cause of
intense local concern in view of its damage to amenity and marine
habitats. But for the cost constraint and lack of suitable
land-based alternatives, the NCB would like to bring such tipping
to an end (Ref.2).

Various working parties (Ref.14) between DoE, NCB and local authorities have been in existence since the early 1970s to consider
how to end beach tipping on the Durham coast. The recommended
solution has been the construction of pipelines to deposit waste
500 metres or so out to sea and several detailed technical studies
on the practicalities of this solution were conducted in the late
1970s for the NCB. As a result, an experimental hydraulic pipeline
has now been constructed at Horden Colliery taking sized (to 40mm)
coarse discard and tailings out to sea. This was the first scheme
to receive financial support from the DoE under the £2½ million
budget set aside for innovative spoil disposal projects in the May
1983 White Paper. It will enable a full assessment to be made of
the distance at which dispersal is adequate, the extent of any
adverse impacts on the local marine environment and the strength of
the pipeline to withstand the conditions of the North Sea.

7.6   Transport Methods for Off-site Disposal

Tipping into voids involves the same basic handling processes of
transfer from CPP, placement and compaction. The difference lies
in the distances that may be involved in the transfer element. In
some cases these may be little more than those involved in on-site
disposal. There are, however, as yet, no practical examples of
remote spoil disposal schemes (over 15kms), only feasibility
studies. The practicality of different transport modes for
carrying spoil over these distances can, however, be inferred from
the experiences of other industries involving bulk haulage,
including coal itself.

At the disposal site a similar range of earth moving equipment as
described for on-site operations would be required.

The main forms of off-site transport are those using public access
routes such as road, rail and canal.

Road

The standard vehicle for use with dry discard on public roads is a
rigid bodied, four axle tipper conforming to The Motor Vehicles
(Construction and Use) Regulation 1978 (as amended) with a maximum
payload of 20 tonnes. New vehicles taking advantage of the
increase in maximum gross weight have a payload up to about 24
tonnes. Wet discard may be transported in road tankers.

7.6 cont'd

A low level of capital investment is required in lorries and
capacity can be readily increased or decreased by purchase or hire.
There is little fixed infrastructure required at either the
colliery or disposal point. Additionally, the extensive road
network, maintained at national expense, allows flexibility of
routeing unless controls are imposed by the Highway or Planning
Authority.

Road transport is, however, subject to disruption by bad weather
and is expensive on labour and fuel consumption. In environmental
terms it can cause disturbance to residents en route and to other
road users. Potential problems of dust and spillage can be reduced
by wheel washing and sheeting. The NCB may be asked to contribute
towards the cost of highway improvements and/or maintenance in some
circumstances.

Rail

Movement of colliery spoil by rail requires specialist handling
equipment at the disposal point. There are currently two types of
rail wagon. One is fitted with bottom discharge doors and the
other is a box wagon which requires upturning by a specialist wagon
tippler for discharge. The former is used in the Nelson Bog
disposal scheme in South Wales and for unloading onto the beach in
the North East. The latter method is not currently used by the
NCB.

Bottom discharge wagons experience difficulty due to sticky or
frozen material whilst a tippler device is expensive. Recently,
the Standard Railway Wagon Co. Limited has built a side tipping
wagon which could be used at conventional sidings with the
construction of a low (450mm) discharge wall, eliminating the
expense of either hoppers or tipplers.

This new wagon has a hydraulic ram on one side between the box and
the chassis. Activation of the ram tilts the box body to facilitate discharge of the material contents. Wagons have been
designed for 90 tonnes gross laden weight. Successful trials of a
prototype wagon were conducted in November 1983 involving the NCB
Doncaster Area and (British Rail) BR Scientific Department.

Although many collieries are already rail connected, few disposal
sites can be expected to be readily equipped, although some larger
worked out mineral sites have rail connections. Loading and
unloading facilities represent a high capital investment only
likely to be justified for large quantities of spoil travelling to
a disposal site over a long period of time. Fitting additional
trains into existing schedules may sometimes be a problem on main
lines.

Discretionary grants are available under Section 8 of the Railways
Act 1974 to meet up to 50% of the capital cost of new private
sidings. This measure is designed to encourage the transfer of
freight to rail where environmental benefits can be expected. Rail
transport of spoil might generally be preferred against road
transport over long distances on both environmental and energy
saving grounds, although overall costs of rail transport may often
be higher.

7.6 cont'd

Inland Waterway

Canals offer another alternative for transport of spoil although few collieries or disposal sites are located directly on the waterway system and transhipment facilities are expensive to provide and operate. There are three types of vessel: push-tow (as predominantly used for coal), pull-tow and self-propelled barges. Capacities are mostly in the range of 150-500 tonnes.

The advantages of this mode of transport are due to high productivity and low energy costs which may give rise to overall cost savings compared to diesel powered rail. Loading facilities may be simple to provide and a quick turn-around is not essential due to low demurrage. Unloading is less easy, usually necessitating a grab but sometimes a tippler. Grants may be available for new waterside installations under the 1981 Transport Act.

Dedicated Transport

Three forms of dedicated transport are theoretically available for off-site transfer: conveyors, pipelines and aerial ropeways. There are current examples of the NCB using the first two modes but only for relatively short distances off-site. These dedicated modes tend to be relatively inflexible and are only economical when operating at their rated capacity. Once installed though, subsequent manpower requirements are minimal. Wayleaves (i.e. rights of access across land) need to be negotiated and paid for.

i] Conveyors

Long distance conveyors can either be reinforced rubber belts or cable belts. The latter are used underground by the NCB to transport coal; those planned for Selby having a single length of 15 kilometres. To avoid severance on the surface, conveyors can be laid in sunken ducts at a cost, or laid along existing rights of way.

ii] Pipelines

There are two main forms of pipeline dependent upon the carrying medium: hydraulic which usually uses water and pneumatic which uses air. In addition, there are several types of pumping mechanism which can affect the stage length and size of particle carried. Their application to the movement of solids like colliery spoil is currently limited although various research projects are under way. Abrasion can be a problem.

Hydraulic pipelines are regularly used for transporting fines discard as a slurry. Only one coarse slurry pipeline has been installed to date and that is the experimental 255mm pipeline out to sea in operation at Horden since 1978. This experiment aims to find the most suitable method of pumping and the most durable pipe

7.6 cont'd

lining materials. Parallel research has been undertaken at Cran-
field into lining materials. The Transport and Road Research
Laboratory (TRRL) has also undertaken experiments with Warwickshire
colliery spoil using a 156mm diameter pipe (Ref.15). Severe
degradation of the spoil took place and whereas this improved the
operating characteristics of the pipeline, subsequent dewatering
and placement of the material was more difficult (although
irrelevant if being pumped to sea).

There are two forms of hydraulic technology that are also causing
interest: dense phase and hydraulic capsule. The former involves
pumping large particles in a dense slurry of fines with a high
specific gravity. Water content is reduced which may make
subsequent dewatering easier, and energy requirements and wear
rates are reduced. BP Coal are currently researching this method
and initial laboratory work and field trials indicate that costs
may be competitive with conventional transport over distances of
over 100km. BP are experimenting with the use of oil as the
carrying medium which could be burnt as a fuel with the coal at the
destination, thus eliminating the need for return systems. It is
doubtful if such a medium would be viable for spoil.

Hydraulic capsule pipelines involve the encapsulated freight being
suspended and driven by a pumped liquid. Experiments are taking
place in Canada but there are no commercial installations yet.

Pneumatic pipelines, are already used by the NCB to propel coal
underground as for example at Shirebrook Colliery. Range limitations and high wear rates currently constrain the use of such
systems over long distances.

Investigations are being carried out to use pnematic pipelines to
transport bulk solids in a dry state within capsules in the
pipeline. The main advantage of this system over slurry pipelines
is that no water (carrying medium) is used which removes the
problem of treatment and disposal at the receiving end. Wear from
abrasion is also substantially reduced. The British Hydro-
mechanics Research Association (BHRA) has conducted specific
studies on the feasibility of transporting spoil using this
technology. In particular it looked at the possibility of transporting colliery spoil to Spurn Bight or Broomfleet from the
Yorkshire coalfield for the Regional Waste Disposal Working Group
in 1978 (Ref.16). In 1981, William Press, one of the industrial
organisations which, together with the DTp, financed an experimental test loop at Milton Keynes, acquired the licence to exploit
the pneumatic capsule pipeline system commercially and to carry out
further development. Following discussions with the NCB, William
Press designed a pneumatic capsule pipeline system to transport
colliery spoil from Kellingley Colliery to the CEGB ash disposal
scheme at Gale Common, North Yorkshire, a distance of about 2
kilometres to replace the current road transport system. A
proposal for financial assistance was submitted to the EEC but
failed.

7.6 cont'd

iii] <u>Aerial Ropeways</u>

An alternative continuous delivery system to either conveyors or pipelines is aerial ropeways. Modern bicable systems are capable of traversing long distances in flights of up to 10 kilometres. They have advantages in rugged terrain but create maintenance access difficulties,are subject to climatic problems and may be visually intrusive. They are not currently used for spoil in the UK.

8.0 <u>RESTORATION AND AFTERCARE</u>

8.1 <u>Introduction</u>

In accordance with the definitions given in the DoE's "Green Book" (Ref. 17) restoration is taken to be the process from final tipping to placement of top-soil and aftercare to be from initial planting to the end of a five year maintenance period. Together the two processes are termed reclamation, although in common usage reclamation means recovering derelict land to productive use.

Ultimately, the restoration practices adopted for individual schemes are determined by the type of after-use to be achieved. Where the after-use is general open space amenity, vegetation may be established into the bare spoil in which case the restoration processes will be restricted to ameliorative measures, such as ripping/tining and mulching. Where tree cover is sought preparations will include relieving compaction and utilising available soil-forming materials.

Where the intended after-use is arable cultivation, the main emphasis of restoration after ripping and liming of the underlying spoil is on replacement of soil and its treatment and management. Top- and sub-soil are often in short supply, particularly on old colliery spoil disposal sites, which reduces the potential for cultivation.

The landform design of a tip should be influenced by the landform of the surrounding landscape. The intended after-use will also be an important determinant of the side slopes. Level surfaces lead to drainage problems and should be avoided, working to a preferred minimum gradient of 1 in 15. Generally, for arable land, slopes should not exceed 1 in 8. Steeper slopes of up to 1 in 3 can be restored to permanent pasture; even steeper slopes can be tree planted (Ref. 8).

Disposal sites can also be reclaimed to other after-uses, for example industrial or housing, providing adequate site preparation is undertaken and essential infrastructure and services installed. Such uses are not considered further here although they can have agricultural implications by diverting development pressure from good quality farmland elsewhere.

Although the main emphasis of this chapter is on new disposal sites, it is recognised that the restoration and aftercare processes are equally applicable to post 1974 GDO tips (see Section 10.2). Reclamation of pre-1974 GDO tips is usually undertaken by Local Authorities using DLG monies. However, in certain instances, these can be included within the boundaries of new tipping sites.

8.0 cont'd

8.2 Restoration Techniques on Bare Spoil

In terms of soil-forming characteristics, colliery spoil is not an ideal medium for supporting plant growth. It is a naturally variable material which, once exposed to weathering and leaching, undergoes rapid and fundamental physical and chemical changes. Wide variations can occur, between tips, between different areas of the same spoil heap and with depth.

Physical

For plant growth spoil generally lacks structure and texture which impairs its moisture holding capacity. The nature of the material and the deficiency of organic matter mean that it is prone to compaction by wheeled machinery. This compaction inhibits the root growth of vegetation by reducing air and water permeability.

Because of the dark colour of colliery spoil, it absorbs heat in warm weather and can cause severe temperature stress to surface vegetation.

Chemical

Iron pyrite is usually the most reactive mineral in spoil. Its weathering follows a complex path of which acidity, ochre and salinity are the most obvious end products, all of which can affect the extent of plant establishment and growth success rates given the varying degrees of sensitivity of different species.

When tipped, fresh spoil is usually neutral or slightly alkaline with a pH value of 7 or 8. In the presence of air and water, the pyrite oxidises causing the pH of the spoil to decrease and create high acidity levels in the surface weathering zone. The rate of acid production depends on the amount and form of the pyrite, the drainage characteristics of the tip and the amount of carbonate minerals present to counter the reaction.

The effect of active pyrite in spoil can result in extreme cases in acidity with pH values as low as 2. These levels cannot generally support plant growth.

Certain colliery discards contain significant amounts of sodium chloride to which plants are sensitive to varying extents. In spoil with low concentrations most plants can survive. Generally the higher the concentration, the more selective the choice of plants has to be and the higher the risk of plant injuries and retardation. Few species can survive in spoil which high concentrations.

Colliery waste is deficient in plant nutrients such as nitrogen, which encourages plant top growth, phosphorus, which promotes root development and potassium, an element essential to plant growth.

8.2 cont'd

Amelioration

Improvement of the physical structure of spoil is assisted by ripping/tining the surface layer of the spoil. This ensures that the top layer of the spoil is as loose as possible. It should be carried out in dry ground conditions to as great a depth as possible. Winged ripping tines are the most effective type of machinery for this operation. The structure of the spoil can further be improved by soil conditioning, for example by the incorporation of organic materials such as farmyard manure and certain sewage sludges. These will improve the texture of the spoil and its capacity to retain moisture. In the absence of soil or other soil-forming materials, the spoil surface can be mulched. This will aid moisture retention and erosion resistance as well as reducing heat absorption.

Acidity levels in colliery spoil are neutralised by adding lime in the form of limestone. This is usually done if the pH value is less than 6. If insufficient lime is added problems may re-occur as further pyrite oxidises. Where large quantities of lime are required, calcitic limestone rather than dolomitic limestone should be used to avoid creating or adding to salinity problems.

In some extreme cases, where pyritic sulphur is present at concentrations greater than 5%, overspreading with less pyritic spoil or other material may be more effective and economical than limestone treatment.

There is no chemical treatment to overcome salinity. However, sodium chloride is soluble and is naturally removed from the surface layers of the spoil when exposed to weathering. However, prolonged exposure, particularly in the summer months, results in the salts being drawn towards the surface. The installation of local sub-surface drains can reduce the damage to vegetation establishment.

Nutrient deficiency is generally overcome by the use of compound fertilisers but farmyard manure and treated sewage sludges in various forms are used when available. The depth of spoil to which these are added will depend on the type of vegetation to be established. To ensure nutrient supplies to the rooting zone of vegetation, sufficient phosphorus and nitrogen for example, should be added to exceed the absorption capacity of the spoil.

8.3 Restoration Techniques using Soil Forming Materials

There are three main processes concerning soil treatment and replacement, all of which should be carried out in dry weather, usually in the summer. Such techniques are essential where the intended after-use is arable cultivation.

8.3 cont'd

a] Soil Stripping and Storage : Top-soil is the main supplier of organic matter, micro-organisms and mineral nutrients. Sub-soil is the main store of water, particularly for summer crop growth. Before stripping the site, a full soil survey is recommended. Efforts should be made to identify any potential soil-forming materials at accessible levels to supplement existing soil supplies.

Soils are generally stripped using motorised scrapers. They should only be stripped in dry conditions (normally between May and September) otherwise soil structure can be seriously damaged. The different types of soil and soil-forming materials should be stripped in layers and stored separately.

Long term storage of materials, especially top-soil, increases the risk of soil deterioration and compaction. It is also expensive in terms of land take and double handling costs. For these reasons progressive restoration is favoured.

Careful design and maintenance of top-soil and sub-soil heaps is necessary to preserve the soil's biological activity and soil structure. Soil heaps should be deposited over large areas to give the maximum surface area subject to land availability. Ripping and sowing with low maintenance grass seed mixtures is good practice;

b] Soil Replacement : Soil replacement is normally carried out by motorised scrapers, bulldozers equipped with ripping tines and sometimes dump trucks. Care needs to be taken to minimise compaction during placement of layers. Lime and fertiliser can be progressively incorporated into the layers during the ripping operations. The final ripped surfaces are then disc harrowed to produce a relatively smooth restored surface.

Soil replacement should be planned to accord with intended after-use. It is not always a case of spreading the stored material evenly across the whole tip. For full arable use one should aim for approximately 300mm of top-soil and 900mm of sub-soil and suitable soil-forming materials. Where these are not available it may be preferable to spread a thin layer of material over sites with little potential, such as north facing slopes, and return these to grass or trees, and to concentrate good depths of material on those parts of better potential, such as south facing slopes, for arable use;

c] Soil Drainage : Prior to construction, any existing ground water drainage will normally be maintained by provision of a piped system. During construction tips are provided with surface system and perimeter drains. The run-off rate from bare spoil is initially high. This rate will reduce during restoration with the establishment of surface vegetation, by a factor of two or more.

8.3 cont'd

Progressive Restoration

This is a recent restoration practice being promoted on sites where conditions permit. It involves restoration progressively following behind tipping operations and is a practice which requires careful forward planning and control of tipping operations. It does not necessarily mean restoration in annual phases. As the NCB notes, this would be impractical in many cases as such small areas of land would be involved.

In the first phase, soil-forming materials are stripped, stored in heaps or screen mounds and are treated, cultivated and maintained. Spoil tipping is then commenced on the stripped area. As tipping progresses towards the final profile, soil is stripped from the phase two area and is 'immediately' re-used on the phase one spoil tip, which can then be restored.

This pattern is followed on subsequent phases until the tipping operations are completed. The soil-forming materials stripped from the phase one area are then used for the completion of the restoration.

The advantages of progressive restoration are as follows:-

-   Tip restoration is not left until the last stage of the disposal operations, when a spoil tip will be at its maximum extent and in an unrestored state. In visually sensitive locations, progressive restoration can be used to great effect by minimising the length of time during which despoilation is evident. With careful planning it may be possible to tip and restore, at an early stage, areas which will screen off subsequent phases of tipping operations. As well as relieving problems of visual intrusion, other pollutants/nuisances such as dust and noise may also be ameliorated;

-   The minimum amount of productive land or amenity land is out of use at any one time, because land is only taken when necessary as the tip advances. In the meantime, completed sections of the tip can be restored and prepared for after-use in advance of the overall tipping operations being completed. Single handling of top- and sub-soil has cost savings and reduces damage to soil structure;

-   Water pollution control can also be assisted. Progressive restoration has the effect of reducing the risk of pollution by reducing the quantity of run-off and limiting the area of exposed spoil.

Progressive restoration is easier to achieve on a coarse or mixed discard tip rather than where lagoons are present. It can be effectively achieved where handling is done by stacker spreader as was argued at the South Kirkby Public Inquiry. In some locations though, the NCB argues that small areas of land make progressive restoration impractical.

8.0 cont'd

8.4 Restoration of Lagoons

Where lagoons are used, although early restoration of the banks will generally be possible, restoration of the remaining area has to wait until the lagoon has completed its operational life and has dried out.

Although the NCB acknowledges that lagoons involve more land being out of use at any one time than coarse discard/pressed cake tips, it stresses that the differences are not that great. For a hypothetical 100ha. site, lagoons are said to involve an average of 25ha. out of other use at any one time compared to a dry tip involving 12ha. (Ref.22). The value of lost agricultural production arising from the use of lagoons is calculated as representing less than 1% of the additional costs of using pressing equipment (Ref.13).

Lagoons do not unduly delay restoration according to the NCB. The only delay is in the final capping or overtipping of the lagoon after it has gained sufficient strength. In support of this argument the NCB (Ref.8) point to the results of a recent survey in four Areas which show that overtipping of most lagoons had started within two years of the cessation of pumping and, in most cases, was completed within a further two years (Table 8.1). Timing at individual collieries will, however, be influenced by the urgency or otherwise of the need to overtip and the availability of coarse discard.

TABLE 8.1

TIME TAKEN TO OVERTIP LAGOONS

No. of Years elapsed between pumping ceasing and overtipping	Number of Lagoons				
	North Yorks.	North Derbys.	South Notts.	North Notts.	Total
1	11	2	5	5	23
2		1	9	6	16
3	2		5		7
4		1	1	2	4
5			1		1
6					
7					
8+	2			3	5

8.4   cont'd

Duration of Overtipping	Number of Lagoons				
	North Yorks.	North Derbys.	South Notts.	North Notts.*	Total
1	11	2	7	4	24
2	4	2	8	2	16
3			2	2	4
4			2		2
5			1		1
6			1	1	2

*7 in progress

Source : Table reproduced from Ref.8

The MPAs state (Ref.23) that, in general, the agricultural land loss is much greater with lagooning than admitted by the NCB. In Nottinghamshire, where lagooning is the main method of fines disposal, the average amount of land out of agricultural use for all tipping in 1982 was 49% of the NCB's permitted area. (Note that other factors have affected this legacy besides methods of fines disposal.) This compares with the maximum of 7½% which was considered feasible in the North East Leicestershire coalfield where 100% mechanical dewatering was proposed.

According to Nottinghamshire County Council greater delays on restoration can be expected where lagoons are used because:-

    i]   lagoons cannot be overtipped immediately, particularly when they are large;

    ii]   more than one lagoon is normally required in practice, one being built, one being filled and one drying out. This increases the number of active tipping sites in any one tip as, although course discard is used to build lagoon banks, it may also be being tipped in separate locations;

    iii]   phasing of lagoons and coarse discard tips can be difficult. For example, restoration of a coarse discard tip can be delayed if coarse discard (in short supply) has to be used to build a bank for lagoons. Lack of coarse discard may mean changes in the original scheme which might result in fewer and much larger lagoons and more unrestored areas at any one time than originally planned;

    iv]   shaping can be much more problematic, giving rise to engineered landforms which may be aesthetically unpleasant;

8.4 cont'd

    v] introduction of lagoons, where not originally included in the tip design, can result in reduced capacity overall for discard and hence increased land take;

   vi] lagoons sometimes have to be taken out of use temporarily to allow mining to take place beneath active lagoons.

8.5 <u>Aftercare</u>

In the Minerals Act 1981, aftercare is defined as "planting, cultivating, fertilising, watering, drainage or otherwise treating of land."

To different degrees, these activities are required whether for the treatment of bare spoil or utilisation of top-soil and sub-soil. These processes are described as follows:-

a] Vegetation establishment techniques : Most reclamation schemes initially result in spoil heaps being grassed over either as a temporary measure to improve soil structure in preparation for use as arable land, or as a permanent measure for grazing, mowing for hay/silage or recreational use. The most important requirement for establishment of grass is a good seed bed tilth. Normal seed bed preparation practices consist of ploughing, disc harrowing and chain harrowing. After fertilising and cultivation, grass seed is usually sown by either 'drilling' the seed into the prepared seed bed or by 'broadcasting' onto the bed using fertiliser distributors.

On steep slopes hydroseeding may need to be considered. In this technique, seed and fertiliser are mixed and sprayed on the ground in a liquid medium, which includes mulch, lime, fertiliser and usually a suspension stabiliser in water. The problems with this technique are that the seed remains much more vulnerable to climatic variations and is susceptible to the toxicity of fertilisers and lime at high concentrations.

The selection of seed type and mixture depends on site conditions and the proposed land use type. Seed type and mixtures range from amenity grassland seed, including wild flowers, to grass and legume. Seed mixes for pastureland need to be hardy to withstand weed invasion and grazing, and high in nutritional value.

Both the Universities of York and Newcastle have conducted research, on behalf of DoE, into the establishment and maintenance of herbaceous vegetation for agricultural and amenity after-uses. Both studies have involved setting up and monitoring trial plots. The York research (Ref.18) has concentrated on nutrient problems of vegetation and the evaluation of different grass and legume cultivars. The Newcastle research (Ref.19) has concentrated on the characteristics of soil-forming materials in relation to vegetation

8.5 a] cont'd
establishment, including soil depth, structure and chemistry.
Other research, partly sponsored by the NCB from the Welsh
Plant Breeding Station, has been monitoring sheep grazing on
trial grass plots at a South Wales Colliery.

The NCB has also, since 1982, been investigating the practical
aspects of tip restoration with and without available soil
cover through sponsored projects with the Midlands Research
Unit based at the School of Agriculture, University of Nottingham. This work has comprised surveys of existing
restoration and the monitoring of on-going schemes and special
field-scale trials. When completed the work will form the
basis of a revised edition of the NCB Notes for Guidance on
Tip Restoration.

Trees and shrubs are planted on colliery spoil for a variety
of reasons including screening cover on steep slopes, wind
breaks and shelters, to encourage wild life habitats, as
commercial forestry or for general amenity purposes. The
ability of trees to tolerate exposed positions and adverse
ground conditions means that they are of particular use on
sites where soil-forming materials are limited and on steep
slopes where other uses are not practical.

The preparations required prior to planting are operations to
relieve compaction, liming, phosphate application and
fertilising. Planting operations are carried out between
October and March.

To achieve the best results in terms of establishment rate and
effect, trees and shrubs should be planted as small as possible and in large numbers. Forestry transplants and whips are
ideal for use on spoil heaps.

The Forestry Commission has conducted research for DoE into
engineering and cultivation practices aimed at achieving high
tree growth and survival on regraded colliery spoil (Ref.20).
NCB is focussing its research efforts on the practical factors
affecting the successful establishment and growth of trees and
shrubs.

Once planted, tree and shrub areas will need to be fenced to
protect them against animals and people. In addition, initial
maintenance of the plants may be needed in the form of
watering, fertilising, weed control and pruning.

Direct tree seeding is a comparatively new technique by which
tree seeds are mixed with mulches and fertilisers and mechanically sown. Research and field work have been carried out by
Cambridge University on behalf of the Scottish Development
Agency into the feasibility of establishing scrub and woodland
on Scottish coal and oil shale tips by direct seeding. The
research included monitoring trial plots (Ref.21). The
potential development of this technique could resolve many
problems in terms of achieving swift and economic establishment of indigenous vegetation onto colliery spoil heaps on a
large scale basis;

8.5 cont'd

b] Field Drainage : MAFF maintain that installation of water supplies and field drainage systems are essential to agricultural after-use involving crop production. Such systems consist of main outlet drains fed by lateral drains under the whole area. Secondary drainage treatments, for example sub-soiling/mole ploughing, may need to be repeated during the 5 year aftercare period. Advice on the need for drainage and design of a system is usually obtained from MAFF Land and Water Service.

NCB maintains that the need for field drainage systems depends upon side slopes and the nature of the soil;

c] Management : This is an essential aspect of good reclamation practice and involves the maintenance after planting. It will ensure continuing health and growth of established vegetation and the build-up of structure, biological activity and fertility of soils.

Even areas eventually intended for arable use, are normally put down to grass for the first few years. Above normal applications of compound fertilisers will be required initially to establish a good grass sward and annually there-after. Controlled grazing improves soil structure and fertility by encouraging tillering and root growth and by providing natural manuring. Other practices which may be used include grass cutting for hay or silage.

Amenity grassland, where grazing and silage production is not possible, will normally receive maintenance such as cutting/mowing, weed control and applications of fertiliser and lime. These operations will control the development of the soils and the visual appearance and health of the vegetation cover.

Tree planted areas usually require maintenance practices such as suppression of invasive/competitive grass and weeds by application of chemical sprays, pruning and thinning, promoting the health, appearance and canopy spread of trees, and the application of lime and fertilisers. Normal forestry practices allow for a 12 or 24 month maintenance and replace-ment period. During this period any dead or dying plants are replaced to achieve a 90% (forestry) or 80-90% (amenity) take overall.

8.6 Restoration Achievements in Practice

The NCB believes that any restoration problems largely result from historical circumstances, for example on sites which predated detailed planning controls where soil was not stripped in advance of tipping. On many such sites NCB is applying the results of practical research projects and encouraging vegetation establish-ment into bare spoil. Under more recent planning permissions the NCB does not envisage any problems in meeting its restoration

8.6   cont'd

obligations.   Research on its behalf by the School of Agriculture
at Nottingham University has revealed no problems which require the
application of other than good conventional agricultural practice
albeit on occasions using higher rates of ameliorants and equipment
of larger capacity and power than is common in farming.   The NCB
maintains that in some cases spoil tipping can improve the quality
of low-lying poorly drained land.

MAFF maintain however that even with advances in restoration techniques, the productivity of land once restored to agriculture will
rarely reach the same standard as that of the original land.   There
are a combination of technical reasons for this which relate to
factors such as availability of soil-forming materials, the
structure of re-used soils, the biological activity in soils,
drainage and maintenance.   The loss of agricultural land may be
redressed in terms of area but in terms of quality it is at least
semi-permanent.

Apart from the technical considerations there are also procedural
problems which have to be overcome when restoring land to agricultural use.   Some consider it an advantage for the original farmer
to return to the site after it has been restored but this is not
always practical because the affected farmstead unit may not be
viable during tipping and the farmer may move elsewhere.   This
problem can sometimes be overcome by the NCB arranging land swaps.

An approach is to get a farmer onto the land to act as the Board's
agent.   The Board will usually contribute to bills or undertake
work for the first two to three years and will offer a full
agricultural tenancy when restoration is completed.   Rents are
charged and increased as restoration proceeds and the agricultural
value of the land increases.

A further key issue to the success or failure of any agricultural
restoration scheme is the availability, in sufficient quantities
and to the required standard, of sub-soil and top-soil materials to
cover tips.   The availability of these restoration materials and
the methods by which they are handled and spread is a key factor.
Land drainage is also important and if inadequate provision is made
combined with heavily compacted soils, this can result in
unsuccessful restoration schemes.

Topographical variations do vary from one county to another and can
pose problems for the design and restoration of tips.   Steep slopes
are only suitable for grass cover or tree planting.

Advanced planning is an essential aspect of good restoration and
aftercare practice.   The MPAs generally require the NCB to produce
restoration programmes early in the planning process, which give
details of time scale, storage and quantities of restoration
materials, practices and aftercare proposals etc.   Working relationships between the MPAs and the NCB Areas are well established in
most areas and early consultations are now commonplace.   Extensive
conditions covering restoration and aftercare are generally then
attached to planning permissions.

8.6 cont'd

However, even with careful forward planning and a comprehensive restoration programme, the end results on the ground can only be achieved by well implemented practices. Of the case study sites visited and other tips in surrounding areas viewed, where restoration has taken place, the results appear to be very variable.

An inherent problem with restoration of this type of material and type of operation is that there is a long time span involved from the planning of the restoration through to its implementation, except where progressive restoration is taking place. Situations do change and can result in adjustments being needed to restoration programmes which are not always wholly satisfactory. A variation in disposal operations can result in restoration programmes being delayed and disrupted and subsequently in different results being achieved. In terms of tipping operations and procedures, restoration work can come low on the list of cost and manpower priorities.

The 1981 Minerals Act enables MPAs to impose an aftercare condition covering a period of up to five years on new permissions for waste tips. Some NCB Areas are concerned that MAFF will be unable to cope with the extra workload created by the Act. They are also concerned that this recent legislation might discourage farmers who may fear increased bureaucracy.

Restoration problems are also experienced in other minerals operations and improvements elsewhere have applicability for spoil disposal practice.

Other Mineral Operations

The NCB Opencast Executive has long experience of restoration and aftercare having worked with such statutory obligations since 1958. It is generally recognised as having a good restoration record, particularly in the quality of its restoration methods, machinery and techniques.

The Opencast Executive does have some advantages over Deep Mines in dealing with restoration. Opencast sites generally cover big surface areas worked by large scale civil engineering plant and do not generate any fines discard. Overburden forms a more reasonable sub-strata of use for soil making than does colliery waste and problems of salinity and toxicity are less important. Opencast sites are generally worked and restored on a contract basis but because of the profitability of the industry more resources are available to develop and monitor restoration techniques and practices. The Opencast Executive has strong working relationships with MAFF in the monitoring and aftercare of schemes once completed.

8.6 cont'd

Joint Agricultural Land Restoration Experiments have also been carried out in the sand and gravel industry commissioned by the DoE, MAFF and the Sand and Gravel Association (Ref.24). Progress is being monitored on the restoration of sand and gravel workings on five sites, the earliest two of which commenced in 1974 and are at Papercourt Farm in Surrey and Bush Farm in Essex. These sites were filled with inert and industrial waste between 1975 and 1977. This was followed by initial settlement and soil reinstatement in 1977. The first restorative cropping (grass and winter barley) occurred in 1978. The experiment intends that cropping will continue until 1986 giving at least five years of restorative cropping with the aim of improving soil condition rather than achieving a particular crop yield. The progress reports which are currently available up to 1982 do not yet cover the full period and no firm conclusions to the experiment have yet been made.

Preliminary findings indicate that at Papercourt Farm it was necessary to import soil and this was prone to compaction and restricted drainage within the sub-soil profile. The experiment discovered that it was essential to install land drainage immediately after soil reinstatement, because prolonged waterlogging causes damage to the weakly structured soil. With the aftercare management objective of improving soil conditions, the initial cover of grass was replaced after a time by a winter barley crop which was more effective in extracting moisture through its deeper roots from the sub-soils below 300mm underground.

The problem of drainage was not so significant with the Bush Farm experiment and the pioneer grass cover and root system stabilised the top-soil and upper sub-soils. Within three years a winter wheat crop was sown and gave a very satisfactory performance, with an average yield for the region.

Institutional Review

INSTITUTIONAL REVIEW

9.0   NATIONAL COAL BOARD

9.1   Management Structure

At the time of writing this Final Report (autumn 1985) the NCB is being reorganised. The organisational structure is as follows:-

1.   Headquarters are in London and Doncaster. At HQ are a number of functional departments, such as Finance, Industrial Relations, and Purchasing and Stores. Part of Mining department has moved to Bretby.

2.   The main part of the Board's activities is deep mining. For organisational purposes the country is now divided into ten Areas (The tables in this report reflect the previous structure of twelve Areas).

3.   At Area level most, but not all, of the HQ functional departments are represented. Each Area controls a number of collieries, typically between 10 and 20.

4.   At colliery level the colliery manager is in overall charge. He has reporting to him a number of officials, some of whom also report on a functional basis to relevant Area officials.

5.   In addition to deep mining, there are a number of other operational units. Of relevance to this Project are:

   - Opencast Executive (OE), responsible for all opencast operations;

   - Minestone Executive (ME), responsible for the commercial exploitation of spoil;

   - Operational Research Executive (ORE)(Environment Section), responsible for Operations Research and also advice on environmental assessment techniques.

The organisational structure of the Board was elaborated in Chapter 3 of the Monopolies and Mergers Commission 1983 report (Ref.25) on efficiency and costs. Further detail at a general level can be obtained from that report. The remainder of this section considers only those aspects of the organisation relating to spoil disposal.

The Board does not have a function exclusively devoted to the disposal of colliery spoil. There are a large number of officials throughout the organisation, however, who have responsibility for various aspects of the disposal process as summarised in Figure 9.1. In common with NCB practice, many of these officials are brought together through a series of national and area committees as shown on Figure 9.2 and described below. Organisational information in both Figures shows the position at February 1984. This structure remained for most of the Study period but was being revised in late 1985.

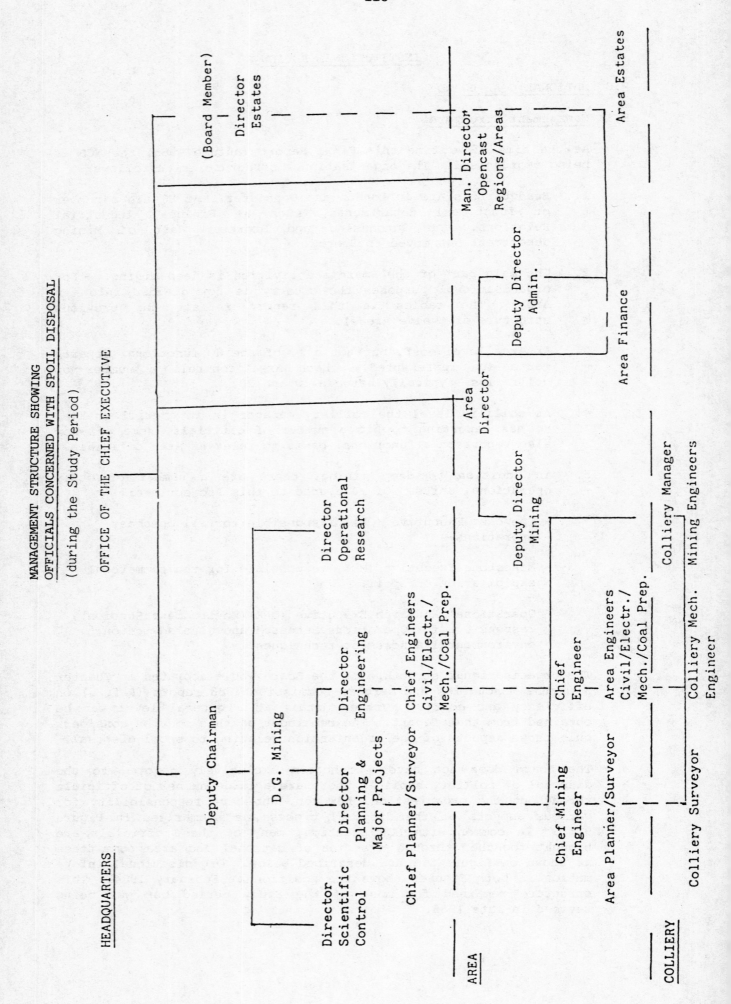

MANAGEMENT STRUCTURE SHOWING
OFFICIALS CONCERNED WITH SPOIL DISPOSAL
(during the Study Period)

FIGURE 9·1

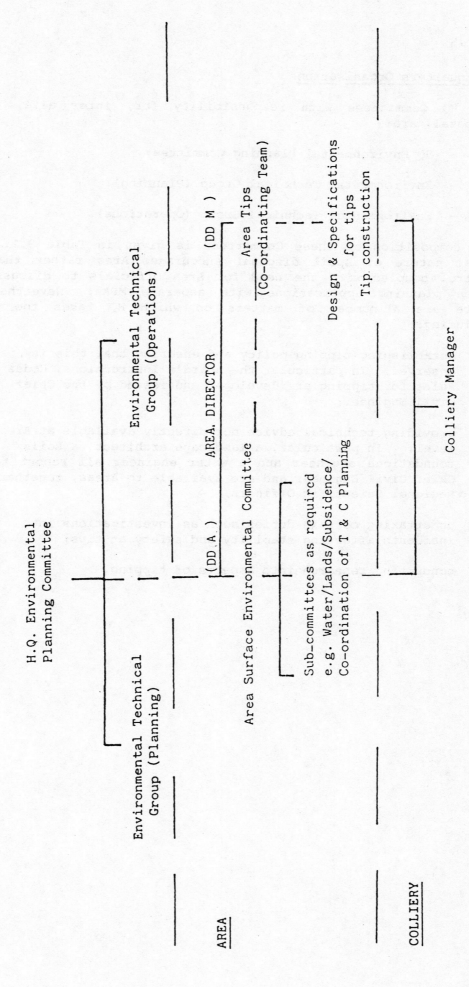

STRUCTURE OF COMMITTEES CONCERNED WITH SPOIL DISPOSAL

(during the Study Period)

FIGURE 9·2

9.1 cont'd

Headquarters Organisation

The HQ Committees with responsibility for, inter alia, spoil disposal, are:-

- HQ Environmental Planning Committee;

- Environmental Technical Group (Planning);

- Environmental Technical Group (Operations).

The composition of these Committees is given in Table 9.1. The local nature of spoil disposal encourages Area rather than HQ control coupled with the need for Area officials to discuss and agree planning applications with separate MPAs. Nevertheless, there are a number of matters on which HQ takes the lead, including:-

- establishing tipping policy and ensuring that this is observed. In particular the Board's Instructions, Codes and Rules for tipping are developed and issued by the Chief Civil Engineer;

- providing technical advice not directly available at Area level. In particular, a landscape architect, a soils/ foundations engineer and a water engineer all report to the Chief Civil Engineer and are available to Areas, together with Regional Scientific Officers;

- undertaking certain duties such as investigations into incidents affecting stability and safety at tips;

- conducting research into aspects of tipping.

TABLE 9.1

COMPOSITION OF HEADQUARTERS COMMITTEES
VESTED WITH RESPONSIBILITY FOR SPOIL DISPOSAL

Officer	HQ Environmental Planning Committee (EPC)	Environmental Technical Group Planning (TCP)	Environmental Technical Group Operations ETC (O)
Deputy Director General Mining	* Chair	* Chair	
Director Engineering	*		*
Deputy Secretary	*	*	
Chief Surveyor	*	*	*
Assistant Chief Surveyor	*	*	*
Operational Research	*		*
Minestone Executive	*	*	
Opencast Executive	*	*	*
Legal Department	*	*	*
Public Relations	*		
Director of Estates	*	*	
Chief Civil Engineer			*
Principal Civil Engineer			*
Director Scientific Control			*
HQ Scientist			*
Finance Department	*		

9.1 cont'd

Area and Colliery Organisation

At Area level, the Area Director is ultimately responsible for all
operational matters including spoil disposal.   In practice the
Area Director delegates spoil disposal policy to the Deputy
Director - Administration (DDA) , who chairs the Surface Environmental Committee, and senior Area officials. Members of that
Committee include most of the Area officials involved in spoil
disposal.   The Surface Environmental Committee is responsible for
policy and planning of disposal (and other matters), whilst
technical and operational responsibility lies with the Tips
Committee (called the Dirt Disposal Committee in some Areas).
Typical compositions of these Committees are given in Table 9.2.

In general terms Area officials are responsible for planning,
acquiring and disposing of tipping sites while the Colliery Manager
has the responsibility for overseeing tipping activity during the
operational stage, although the Area Chief Engineer retains responsibility for technical management.

The four officials at Area level most involved in spoil disposal
are the:-

-    Deputy Director-Administration, who conducts the formal
     liaison with the MPA and appears, where necessary, at Public
     Inquiries;

-    Area Surveyor and Minerals Manager, who identifies the need
     for additional tipping capacity at individual collieries,
     identifies potential sites, discusses these with the MPA and
     statutory undertakers and submits the planning application;

-    Area Civil Engineer, who advises on tip design and the tech-
     nical suitability of tipping sites, co-ordinates the civil
     engineering works in advance of tipping, regularly inspects
     tips at appropriate intervals to comply with legislation and
     supervises restoration including placement of soil;

-    Area Estates Manager, who advises on the practicability of
     obtaining tipping sites, purchases sites, may supervise
     initial planting and aftercare programmes and, where
     applicable, disposes of restored sites.

At the colliery level, while the Colliery Manager is in overall
charge of tip construction, practical control on a day to day basis
is usually exercised by the Surface Superintendent or Colliery
Mechanical Engineer, whose tasks include ensuring that tipping is
undertaken in accordance with planning conditions.

TABLE 9.2

COMPOSITION OF AREA COMMITTEES VESTED WITH
RESPONSIBILITY FOR SPOIL DISPOSAL

Officer	Area Surface Environmental Committee	Area Tips Sub Committee
Deputy Director (Admin)	* Chair	
Chief Mining Engineer	*	
Chief Accountant	*	
Chief Engineer	*	* Chair
Civil Engineer	*	*
Mechanical Engineer		*
Surveyor	*	*
Scientist	*	
Legal representative	*	
Coal Preparation	*	*
Reps. from Opencast/NSF/		
Minestone	*	*
Production Manager		*
Colliery Manager		*

It should be noted that the composition of the above committees can vary
from Area to Area.

9.1 cont'd

Most Areas now operate centralised surface mobile plant pools whereby all NCB earth moving vehicles used in tipping operations are owned and maintained at Area level and provided to individual collieries as the need arises. In some instances, drivers are employed centrally too. Disposal is often carried out by contractors on the Board's behalf.

For advice on various technical aspects of spoil disposal, Areas can call in the help of Regional Scientific Officers (on water, noise, dust pollution, soil properties), ORE Environment section on visual impact, and the HQ landscape architect and HQ Civil Engineer (Environment). One Area (Western) has its own landscape architect and another (South Wales) has in the past used consultant landscape architects. In addition, Areas may make use of consultants in the presentation of evidence at Public Inquiries.

Whilst the above is a generalised description of the officials involved and the associated Committee structure, it must be noted that practice varies between Areas. Statutory duties do not vary, but the Board's policy of delegation leaves considerable power with Area Directors and their subordinates. For example, different Areas have different organisational structures with regard to the management of surface operations. Those differences in structure feed back to differences in the way in which the Surface Environmental Committee and/or the Tips Committee discharge their responsibilities.

Opencast Executive

The OE is responsible for all opencast operations. For operational purposes it is divided into six regions. All opencast production is carried out by contractors and the OE is responsible for planning and maintaining a programme of works and supervising such contracts.

The OE and NCB Deep Mines have liaison arrangements to ensure that every opportunity is taken for deep mine waste to be disposed of into opencast voids. The triggering action usually comes from Deep Mines putting forward spoil disposal plans and OE then responding where suggested sites will affect future possibilities of extracting opencast reserves. The liaison takes place through the Area Surface Environmental Committee and the Tips Committee.

It is often the case that, where proposed tipping sites could affect opencast reserves, it is necessary although inconvenient for the OE to disrupt its own programme of working in order to exploit the reserves which are at risk of sterilization. However, the OE accepts the need for such changes in programme to facilitate spoil disposal. The costs of preparing and subsequently restoring a joint site are allocated as appropriate between the two parties depending on the particular site and scheme.

9.1 cont'd

Minestone Executive

The ME promotes the commercial use of all non-coal products produced by deep and opencast mining. These include minestones (unburnt colliery spoil), burnt shales, surface minerals and mineral by-products.

The Marketing Section is divided into seven regions. Field representatives in these areas provide advice to potential users of colliery waste, including highway and other works authorities, water authorities, and civil engineering and building contractors. Commercial disposals are made by letting contracts to work the spoil deposits.

The Technical Services Group in the ME HQ at Whitburn carry out research and development. Through their efforts a British Standard on the utilisation of waste has recently been issued (BS 6543 : 1985).

Operational Research Executive

ORE was called upon to assemble information on environmental issues during the later stages of the CENE investigation. The Environment Section has since completed work for the HQ Environmental Planning Committee on both waste disposal and the planning of new mines. In particular, it was responsible for the production of guidelines on environmental assessment which were distributed to Areas in November 1981. More recently it produced the environmental checklist which all Areas are encouraged to complete before submitting planning applications for spoil disposal schemes (as described in the next section). Instruction in the use of this checklist has been given by way of seminars for Area staff.

The Environment Section provides an environmental impact assessment service to the Areas. In particular it operates a photo-montage service and computer expertise in drawing visual intrusion maps. It also uses computer techniques for demonstrating sieve map techniques as an aid to locational decision making.

9.2 Planning Procedures

All NCB Areas try to maintain several years of tipping capacity for each colliery or group of collieries, although the ease and success with which they achieve this varies immensely, partly due to the pressures on land and partly due to the relationship between the Area office and the MPA.

K

9.2   cont'd

The process of site selection, receipt of planning permission and detailed design for a new disposal scheme typically takes about five years. In those Areas where there are established liaison arrangements, the MPA is likely to be consulted fairly early in these proceedings. The Evaluative Framework seeks to encourage the widespread adoption of this process.

When a particular scheme has been identified potential land areas are earmarked. Land, if not already owned by the NCB, may be purchased at this stage, especially if it is considered that the proposal will have a reasonable chance of success; or an option on the land may be taken, subject to the successful outcome of a planning application. In some Areas, potentially useful plots of land are bought speculatively as they come onto the market. This land may later be used for tipping, or it may be used in exchange for more suitable land and thus may help ensure an existing farm's viability.

During the initial design process various external consultations are usually made to ensure that as many issues as possible are resolved before the formal submission of a planning application. This will include the Water Authority to check the presence of any sensitive features such as aquifers and the extent of any special preventative measures necessary to control the quality of effluent discharged into a water course; MAFF in terms of the quality of land on the proposed site and any special restoration methods recommended. Some Areas like to consult other bodies such as local amenity groups and the Nature Conservancy Council at this stage; others leave these consultations until after the submission of the planning application.

Before a formal planning application is submitted NCB Areas are encouraged to go through the environmental checklist procedure. This was issued to Areas in 1981 by NCB HQ with advice to use it on spoil disposal schemes. More recently a formal instruction has been issued requiring Areas to carry out the procedure on all projects whose capital cost exceeds £0.5 million with a suggestion that it is also conducted "where appropriate" on less costly projects. The £0.5 million figure is the threshold above which NCB projects must be referred to HQ for Board approval. Although spoil disposal schemes rarely fall into this category, for large schemes which include a spoil tip, the Board require the checklist to be used separately for the proposed tip. The checklist, together with accompanying guidance notes is reproduced at Appendix B.

From figures supplied by South Wales Area, the average determination period from submission of planning application to approval for over 50 tipping and other applications made over a twelve year period, was 7 months and ranged between 2 and 20 months.

9.2   cont'd

Three main comments on the planning and consultation process in relation to spoil disposal arose from discussions held with the NCB Area officials:-

i)   Although many Areas thought that they had good working relationships with their MPAs, some hoped for a better technical appreciation of the problems of spoil disposal. Others wished for a clearer understanding of the delegated powers of the MPA officers as informal agreements were some- times reached with officers only to be challenged or overturned by the elected members of the County Council;

ii)   The agreed solution to a spoil disposal scheme is totally dependent upon the availability of land since the NCB has no compulsory purchase powers;

iii)   Because of the difficulty in predicting the volume and type of spoil to be catered for, the planning permission has to allow for changes in the design after formal approval. This is usually in the form of "by mutual agreement" clauses, but implies that the planning process has to be flexible and continuous.

All these issues face other mineral operators as well as the NCB in their dealings with the MPA.

9.3   Tipping and Restoration Procedures

The detailed design of disposal schemes is based on the two documents described in Section 7 : NCB (Production) Codes and Rules : Tips, 1971 and Technical Handbook : Spoil Heaps and Lagoons. The latter is currently being updated to take account of the advances in tip design and restoration that have occurred over the last decade or so.

The intention to tip has to be brought to the attention of the Mines and Quarries Inspectorate whose main concern is tip safety. Since the Aberfan disaster, tips have tended to be designed to a lower overall height, with shallower side slopes and avoidance of high level lagoons.

In terms of the operational stage of tipping, Areas are required to comply with the Codes and Rules (Tips) 1971, with the Colliery Manager having overall responsibility. Where a tip receives spoil from two or more collieries, one colliery will assume responsibility, as decided by the Health and Safety Executive.

Although all surface mobile plant is centralised at Area level there are variations in the degree to which plant is exclusively assigned to individual collieries or programmed to move between collieries. There is also variation in the employment of drivers, some Areas employing them centrally and some at colliery level. Several Areas put spoil transport, handling and tip operation out to contract, the price usually being quoted on a tonne basis or at day rates.

9.3 cont'd

Aspects of tip operation are frequently controlled by planning permissions where conditions lay down the phasing of tipping, the allowable working hours, noise levels and access points (see Chapter 10).

The NCB's "Technical Handbook: Spoil Heaps and Lagoons" gives little specific guidance on landscaping or restoration, only that close co-operation is necessary with the Planning Authority. However, the NCB is pursuing restoration techniques and has now produced "Notes for Guidance on Tip Restoration" (1982); these cover the procedures to be followed in the various activities of soil stripping, storing, replacement and planting. It is under- stood that these notes are currently being incorporated into the Technical Handbook. Methods of calculating surface water run-off flows and ditch dimensions are recorded in NCB's manual "Technical Management of Water in the Coal Mining Industry".

In line with its evidence at the Vale of Belvoir and South Kirkby Public Inquiries, the NCB is laying great emphasis on progressive agricultural restoration (see Chapter 8). As with other aspects of current restoration practice on spoil tips it is too early to judge the practical effects on the ground where the after-use is agri- cultural rather than amenity planting. The NCB is monitoring early arable crop yields (as opposed to land quality) at collieries such as Bentinck and Cotgrave. The NCB normally aims to let out restored land to tenant farmers but manages tree planted areas itself. North Nottinghamshire Area has a small specialist team which performs all planting and aftercare work itself.

The OE with its longer experience of statutory restoration oblig- ations has provided advice to Deep Mines on restoration techniques through publications and NCB seminars. The OE has developed its own specialist equipment and this is available on loan to Deep Mines Areas. In addition the OE commissions its own research on restoration techniques.

9.4 Accounting Procedures

The Board has a well documented and long established system of cost reporting and control. This system is documented in Chapter 3 of the Monoplies and Mergers Commission report (Ref.25). The accounting system is based upon monthly reports which give individual colliery results. These reports, denoted as F 23s, are then aggregated to provide Area and National reports.

The basic format of the colliery report is that it analyses costs into component categories such as manpower, materials, energy and overheads. These cost categories are maintained throughout the reporting process, so that Schedule 6 to the 1984/85 Accounts reports results in a manner which is consistent with aggregation of colliery results. A key feature of the system at all levels is the comparison of actuals against budget and the Board conducts a series of accountability meetings at monthly and quarterly intervals where variances are discussed in depth.

9.4 cont'd

The monthly colliery report is developed from a variety of input sources, including payroll, stores returns, invoices paid and journal vouchers. As with all accounting systems, cost collation and analysis is heavily dependent upon the account coding given to individual items. The system used by the Board is one of mandatory national rules regarding cost identification and clarif-ication. Within these rules, however, there is flexibility as to the degree of sub-analysis possible under each cost category.

The monthly F23 return uses resource categories such as labour, heat light and power rather than activity categories such as faceworking, underground transport and coal preparation. Individual figures on spoil disposal are therefore not reported.

In practice, however, such costs can be made available:-

-       as an addition to the monthly returns, as part of the extra information prepared by the Area Chief Accountant's staff;

-       as part of the quarterly analysis of costs into activities required from Areas by Headquarters;

-       on an ad hoc basis as required.

It is understood that the quarterly functional analysis could include spoil disposal as a separate item, although generally, such costs are subsumed into categories such as coal preparation or surface operations. This is largely because such costs form a relatively small part of total colliery costs and detailed reporting is not therefore required for accountability purposes. If analysed separately such costs will be reported on another form (F425).

The Board has an established accounting function at Area and colliery level. This function can produce ad-hoc reports if required and spoil costs have been analysed on occasion. For example, this has occurred in response to a recent national level survey by HQ Finance Department (see Chapter 12) and as requested by Area officials.

Only one Area, North Nottinghamshire, was found which formally reports spoil disposal costs, i.e. costs of conveyors and place-ment, on a routine basis. This is done by use of the existing cost classification system behind the monthly F23 return, utilising the flexibility noted above to identify tipping costs separately. The North Nottinghamshire system does not report in full all costs associated with spoil disposal, however, as in order to achieve comparability between collieries, certain aspects of disposal, peculiar to one or two collieries, have been deliberately excluded from the reporting system.

9.4 cont'd

Outside North Nottinghamshire, practice varies. For Areas with centrally controlled plant pools such costs could be readily deduced from the monthly reports available to management on the activities of these pools. Cost reporting varies according to the unit deemed to employ drivers; if not employed centrally, their costs appear on the relevant colliery profit and loss account and not on the surface mobile plant profit centre report.

Restoration costs are controlled at colliery level. Area control would allow site works to be planned more efficiently within an annual budget bearing in mind that such work can largely be done only in the summer months. It is understood that the HQ Finance Department has now established a standard system at Area level whereby an annual provision is made at each colliery to cover later restoration costs. Such a provision enables funds to be built up to meet future outgoings thus removing from the Colliery Manager conflict between improving restoration and increasing profit-ability.

10.0 PLANNING AUTHORITIES

10.1 Planning Responsibilties

General

The town and country planning system, set up under the 1947 Act, has the basic objective of reconciling competing demands on the use of land. There are two main features of the system: forward planning and development control.

Forward planning involves the preparation of development plans of two main sorts: firstly Structure Plans, which provide a strategic overview of development at the county level and are produced by County Councils (or in Scotland by Regional Councils); and secondly Local Plans, which indicate land use allocations for smaller areas within the county and are usually produced by District Councils. Subject Plans are a type of local plan some-times produced by County Councils to clarify Structure Plan policies on a particular issue or land use applicable to a number of district areas.

Development control is the process of determining planning applic-ations taking account of the current development plan and other material considerations. All development requires the prior consent of the planning authority, except for certain activities which have permitted development rights under the General Develop-ment Order (GDO). All applications are submitted to the District Council. District Councils determine all applications except those deemed to be county matters, such as mineral planning. Planning permissions can be given subject to the carrying out of certain conditions. Failure to comply with such conditions can result in enforcement action by the local authority. Applicants can appeal against refusals of permission.

The role of the DoE is to oversee the system especially where issues go beyond individual local authority boundaries and are of national or regional significance. The DoE has to approve a county Structure Plan. It can also call in applications or direct a refusal if an application represents a major departure from a development plan. In these circumstances it will usually conduct a Public Inquiry. These may also be held where an applicant has appealed against refusal of an application from a local authority.

Minerals

In the case of minerals the County Council is the body responsible for both forward planning and development control of minerals (under the Local Government Act, 1972). It is known as the Mineral Planning Authority (MPA). Since 1981 the counties have also become the planning authority for waste disposal in England (under the Local Government Planning and Land Act, 1980), but not in Wales. District Councils are consulted in the process of determining minerals applications but do not have formal powers.

10.1 cont'd

When Metropolitan County Councils are disbanded, responsibility for minerals planning in these areas will pass to Metropolitan Districts. This prospect has implications for the efficiency with which specialist minerals and reclamation teams can be expected to continue to operate and the degree to which local issues may seek to override other considerations in disposal decisions.

Minerals policies are usually included in Structure Plans to indicate under what conditions and in which locations applications for mineral extraction are likely to be acceptable. Such policies are designed to influence the way other agencies act in exercising their own areas of responsibility. Structure Plans may also contain operational policies which are related to the executive responsibilities of the County Council, for example, in respect of land reclamation and solid waste disposal. Several MPAs have now produced Minerals Subject Plans. Advisory plans have also been produced at regional level on minerals and waste disposal issues by various voluntary groupings of County Councils. Regional working parties have been set up to deal with aggregates involving the DoE, MPAs and operators.

All mineral operators must apply for planning permission from the MPA "to win and work minerals in, on or under land". The NCB however, along with nationalised industries, statutory undertakers and other interests, has deemed permission for certain activities under the GDO.

Most planning permissions for mineral operations will be granted conditionally; these conditions specify a way of working designed to minimise disturbance to the environment and nearby residents. Conditions specifying the manner in which the site should be restored to an agreed after-use are also now common although absent from or minimal on older permissions.

Recent changes to the operation of the development control system in relation to minerals largely result from a comprehensive review of the subject by the Stevens Committee which reported in 1976. The 1981 Minerals Act gives the MPA greater control over both active and disused mineral workings. One of the main powers given to the MPA is the ability to impose aftercare conditions on new applications where there are also restoration conditions. An aftercare period of five years is usually specified and consultation is required with the MAFF or the Forestry Commission. It is interesting to note that the OE has been subject to both restoration and aftercare conditions since 1958. A further set of powers when commencement orders have been made will be the ability for the MPA to modify permissions or place conditions where no permissions have previously existed and to impose orders (prohibition or suspension) to require site improvements after mineral workings have ceased. In order to decide whether any of these are

10.1 cont'd

appropriate, the MPA has a duty to review every minerals site in its county. Compensation is payable in the event of exercising these powers. Draft provisions on the appropriate scale of compensation have now been established for mineral operations except NCB. The Minerals Act also brings under planning control the removal of minerals from waste tips, although this provision has yet to be enacted.

10.2 Colliery Spoil Disposal

Responsibilities

As for other mineral matters the County Council, as MPA, is the body responsible for processing spoil disposal applications and dealing with the wider policy issues involved in forward planning. In many coalfield areas, mining issues are sufficiently important to warrant the personal involvement of the County Planning Officer. The Minerals officer will usually have specialist knowledge of mining operations, some having previously worked for the NCB. Some authorities, for example, South and West Yorkshire County Councils, employ specialist mining engineers. Any direct works programme of reclamation is usually run from the County Surveyors/Highways department, as are operational aspects of solid waste disposal.

Despite statutory responsibility for spoil disposal resting with the MPA, District Councils may become involved where proposals rouse an unusual degree of public opposition. District Councils in the mining areas of West and South Yorkshire tend to maintain a higher level of interest in spoil disposal than their counterparts in other parts of the central coalfield. For the most part this means liaison with the relevant MPA. Direct contact with the NCB is usually limited to consultations in the preparation of Local Plans.

MPAs usually have regular working relationships with adjoining counties where interests overlap such as where collieries are situated on the boundary. Within the central coalfield the three Yorkshire authorities and Humberside also have a strong regional association which has made several attempts to provide a wider perspective on the problems and possible solutions of spoil disposal (and other wastes). The Yorkshire and Humberside County Councils Association (YAHCCA) strongly rejected the need for a separate regional working party on spoil issues or a regional development agency for reclamation as suggested by CENE.

Regular liaison systems generally exist between MPAs and their nearest equivalent NCB Area. In most cases, working relationships are perceived to be good although there are significant differences considered appropriate in the degree of liaison with the NCB. Where an MPA has one or two collieries in a different NCB Area, the strength of liaison is usually less strong than with its main Area.

10.2 cont'd

Most MPAs are willing to undertake informal negotiations with the NCB in advance of detailed planning application for tipping schemes being prepared and submitted. The fact that there has so far only been two spoil disposal applications taken to Public Inquiry (but several applications withdrawn before determination) is taken as a reflection that these advance negotiations are working. Most MPAs consulted felt that they were able to influence the precise site selection within the NCB constraints of land ownership and physical proximity to the colliery. In cases where the MPA had encouraged the investigation of remote sites, the additional transport cost was the issue defying its adoption. The only instances where the NCB has been prepared to consider non-local sites are where all other solutions immediately adjacent to the colliery had been exhausted. MPAs have had success at influencing the NCB's restoration practice by themselves providing specialist landscape advice.

Some MPAs were concerned at their lack of influence over NCB's decisions on coal preparation plant (both in investment and in subsequent usage) as such decisions affect the amount of wet waste arising. Instances were mentioned of filter presses being available but not used and land previously allocated for coarse discard being given over to lagoons, thus slowing down restoration and requiring the allocation of more tipping land.

Forward Planning

Spoil disposal policies do not feature very significantly in most Structure plans in coalfield areas, although they are becoming more important in later revisions to Structure Plans. In most cases a single policy sets out criteria by which to reduce the environmental disturbance caused by spoil tipping. Most of these Plans were produced in the mid 1970s since when concerns have increased significantly.

Subsequent revisions to Structure Plans have sometimes formalised these concerns. For example later plans often include a policy setting out a presumption against local tipping where viable alternatives exist for remote disposal. Some policies seek to combine deep mined spoil tipping with opencast schemes and other mineral extraction where appropriate.

Few Minerals Subject Plans yet include deep mining and associated spoil disposal aspects. That currently being finalised by Leicestershire County Council does feature these issues and contains policies that seek to impose adequate safeguards (or local agreements) on dirt disposal and to resist tipping on agricultural land.

10.2 cont'd

The most detailed attempt to collate current and forecast information on spoil arisings and assess options for its disposal has
been by YAHCCA in its June 1983 study (Ref. 26). This followed a
similar attempt at regional level in the mid 1970s to forecast the
volume of uncommitted waste of all types in the Yorkshire and
Humberside areas (Ref. 16). Of the various proposals put forward
by local authorities to reduce the pressure on limited local
tipping sites the Welbeck scheme in West Yorkshire and the Pyewipe
proposal on the south side of the Humber Estuary have advanced the
furthest. Nottinghamshire County Council has compiled similar
forecasting information on a colliery basis for its county but does
not see the need to look for regional level solutions yet (it does
however recognise that the easier sites for local tipping are fast
running out).

Development Control

The development control of spoil tipping falls into two categories.
Firstly, land in use for tipping on 1st July 1948 represents
permitted development under class 20 of the GDO whether or not the
area or height of the tip is extended. Because GDO tips have not
been subject to planning controls they generally have no conditions
attached requiring the NCB to restore them. However, an amendment
to the 1977 GDO gave MPAs the power to ask the NCB to submit
tipping schemes for any operational tips. The production of such
schemes was intended to stimulate the NCB into making provision for
the working and restoring of material deposited since April 1974.
In principle, this gave the MPA a new opportunity to influence the
form of operations and restoration on such tips although not all
MPAs have requested schemes to be put forward. Failure to
institute these provisions may, however, have implications for
future eligibility to claim DLG. Further amendments to the GDO are
currently under consideration by the DoE.

Secondly, tipping on new land requires an application for planning
permission. In terms of procedure NCB applications for spoil
tipping are determined in the normal way for county matters, as
illustrated schematically in Figure 10.1. The application is first
registered with the District Council and then handed on to the
County Council as MPA. The MPA handles the formal consultations
with other authorities and statutory undertakers, even though some
of these like MAFF may have previously been contacted by the NCB.
Public meetings may be held if the application is controversial and
the MPA and NCB may jointly take the platform. An officer
recommendation on the application, together with the views of the
District Council, will then be placed for decision before members
of the appropriate County Committee. The NCB may be allowed to
state its case to elected members at Committee meetings although it
is not permitted to participate in debate.

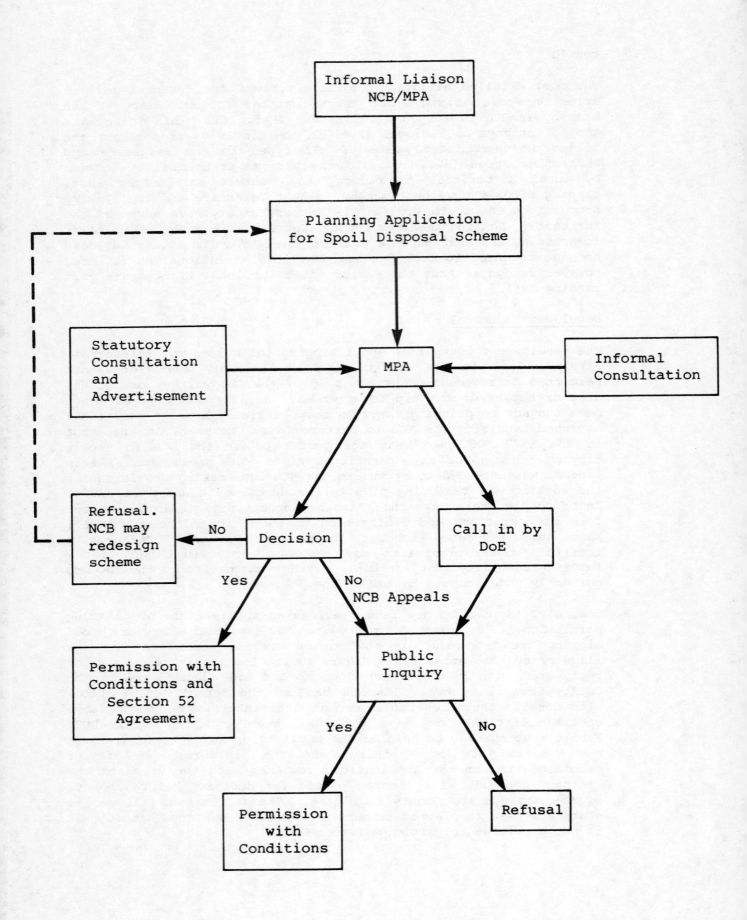

SCHEMATIC ILLUSTRATION OF PLANNING CONTROLS ON NEW SPOIL DISPOSAL SCHEMES

FIGURE 10·1

10.2 cont'd

Reflecting the complexity of spoil disposal issues, the length of
time between receipt of application and decision may be one to two
years compared to the statutory time period of 2 months. Lengthy
negotiations may already have taken place between the NCB and MPA
through regular liaison channels - hence some Areas' rule of thumb
that they begin discussion five years before they need additional
tipping capacity.

In the Yorks, Notts, Derby coalfield more than 100 applications for
tipping schemes have been determined since 1974 (see Table 10.1).
This figure roughly equates with the total number of active
collieries on the coalfield although the applications have been
concentrated on a smaller number of long life pits. All but two of
these were granted conditionally or were approvals of details from
earlier applications. In addition, at least 10 applications were
withdrawn by the NCB before determination, after negotiation with
the MPA, in order to be constructive and avoid the confrontation
that a refusal might bring. The one application that went to
Public Inquiry (South Kirkby) had not been formally determined by
the MPA before the DoE called it in following a recommendation of
refusal by Wakefield District Council.

TABLE 10.1

NUMBER OF TIPPING APPLICATIONS DETERMINED 1974-84

Counties	Approved	Withdrawn	Refused	Temporary	Total
South Yorkshire	38	6	-	5	49
West Yorkshire	32	-	-	-	32
North Yorkshire	2	-	1	-	3
Humberside	1	-	-	-	1
Nottinghamshire	20	-	-	-	20
Derbyshire	11	4	-	-	15
Leicestershire	3	-	1	-	4
TOTAL	107	10	2	5	124

Note: Leicestershire has been included although formally part
          of the South Midlands coalfield.

10.2 cont'd

Conditions attached to spoil tipping permissions usually cover a
wide range of aspects including fencing, landscaping schemes,
tipping schemes, stripping and storage of top-soil and sub-soil,
safeguards with regard to amenity, public footpaths, drainage,
noise, dust, hours of working and, since the 1981 Minerals Act,
aftercare of the restored site for a usual period of five years.
The actual tipping scheme to be agreed usually covers restriction
on the life of the tip, the type of materials to be deposited, the
manner of tipping, restrictions on heights and slopes, phasing of
operations and progressive restoration. The effectiveness of
conditions is considered further in Chapter 15.

The existence of these two types of tipping procedure (deemed
permission under the GDO and planning permissions) sometimes causes
confusion at the margins i.e. each party may put forward a
different definition of the boundary of the GDO tipping site. In
most instances the NCB has been prepared to accept that tipping on
new land immediately adjacent to a GDO tip requires planning
permission. Again in most instances the NCB has been prepared to
allow the application of planning control over that GDO tip
(usually involving the imposition of restoration cond- itions) in
the cause of seeking planning permission for a tip extension. In
this way the NCB has surrendered most of its permitted development
rights on GDO tips. The largest number of remaining GDO tips is in
West Yorkshire.

West Yorkshire County Council has divided its GDO tips into 7
categories:-

   i)   Restored or reclaimed to beneficial use (4 tips);

  ii)   Closed spoil heaps, which could be left with no further
         treatment (5);

 iii)   Closed spoil heaps requiring minimal treatment to return
         them to an environmentally acceptable condition (5);

  iv)   Spoil heaps now used for other purposes e.g. materials
         storage or coal stocking (12);

   v)   Spoil heaps with planning permission (deemed or
         otherwise) for reworking or removal (11);

  vi)   Spoil heaps being reclaimed by the County Council or
         other agencies (2);

 vii)   Active spoil heaps where discussions are being attempted
         with the NCB as regards future tipping and restoration
         arrangements (17).

10.2 cont'd

Tips in the last category cause particular concern and the County
made early attempts to request tipping schemes under the 1977 GDO
amendment. This has led to disagreement over the definition of GDO
site boundaries and some schemes supplied have covered only
continued deposition of material and not restoration. Three tipping
schemes have now been approved. The County has also questioned
whether lagoons are allowed without planning permission on GDO
tips.

Another area that falls outside the development control system is
the re-working of colliery spoil tips. This may be financially
viable if the proportion of coal in old tips (laid down before the
introduction of modern coal preparation plant) is large enough.
This will be brought under control by a provision in the 1981
Minerals Act, but the exception in the case of GDO tips will still
apply.

10.3 Public Inquiries

Public Inquiry experience concerned with spoil disposal issues
largely concerns the Vale of Belvoir and South Kirkby. Both
resulted from the use by the Secretary of State for the Environment
of his call-in powers.

In addition a short Inquiry in 1984 resulted from an appeal by NCB
over refusal of a tip extension at Wernos Colliery in South Wales,
following which permission was given. Spoil disposal issues have
sometimes been discussed at Local Plan Inquiries, for example
provision for future tipping capacity at Markham Main Colliery.

Belvoir was the first Inquiry into a new coalfield development
where spoil disposal was a contentious issue (the Barnsley seam at
Selby being forecast to produce no spoil other than development
dirt). The NCB proposals related to three local disposal sites
adjacent to each of the three new mines (Hose, Saltby and
Asfordby), covering on completion about 600 hectares but with less
than one tenth of the area out of agricultural use at any time.
These tips were designed to take 2.5 million tonnes per annum
lasting 50 to 60 years of the total 75 year production period.

In reaching his recommendation to refuse the tips at Hose and
Saltby, the Inspector placed great importance on their visual
impact. He also concluded that local tipping need not be an
inevitable concomitant of deep mining thus opening the way for
serious consideration of alternatives. The Secretary of State
regarded the visual impact of these two tips in an even more severe
light than the Inspector and, in addition, placed greater weight on
the agricultural objections at the third site, Asfordby. In
refusing permission for overall coalfield development he accepted
that the NCB may wish to submit revised applications (except at
Hose) and proposed that discussion should take place between the
parties into the possibility of remote disposal and underground
stowage as alternatives to local tipping.

10.3 cont'd

Permission has now been given for local tipping in connection with the new mine at Asfordby. An accompanying Section 52 Agreement required that 10% of the annual spoil would be deposited locally off-site and that further quantities would be made available for other local restoration schemes with Leicestershire County Council paying the extra transport costs. The remainder would be deposited on-site unless by March 1985 alternative arrangements for remote disposal had been agreed. No such agreement was in fact reached, but the additional costs of such a solution, as reported by the Remote Disposal Working Party, are discussed in Chapter 12.

South Kirkby was the first Inquiry solely into a tipping proposal at an existing colliery, in the face of District Council opposition supported by strong public unrest from the traditional mining community. The proposal related to 75 hectares on North Elmsall Common physically separated from existing tipping areas by a railway line. The tip was designed to take at least 1 million tonnes per annum over a period of 15 years. According to Wakefield District Council little advance consultation occurred over these proposals.

In presenting its case the NCB placed great emphasis on the investments it had already made in coal preparation plant at the South Kirkby complex. (Since this Inquiry the NCB now require arrangements for spoil disposal to be made in advance of committing such investment). The NCB also stressed the environmental gains to be derived from the use of the proposed stacker spreader, the installation of which would not be justified without a full permission for local tipping. The Secretary of State's decision was to grant permission for Phase 1 of the scheme (8 years capacity) but to require a thorough investigation of alternatives before allowing the NCB to proceed to Phase 2. A working party is now in existence but there are fears that an earlier decision on Phase 2 will be needed in order for the NCB to plan the route of the stacker spreader.

Major Public Inquiries play an important part in the current British planning system by encouraging an open debate on issues of public concern. Because of the wealth of background material produced, Inquiries also have an important educative role for those involved on both the local authority and developer sides. This, together with any concessions on either side made during the course of proceedings, tends to lead to general expectations of higher standards in the determination of subsequent applications of a similar nature in other parts of the country. Local authorities in the older coalfield areas are therefore hoping that many of the environmental safeguards offered by the NCB in respect of tipping schemes in the greenfield situation at Belvoir will be applied at existing collieries.

10.0 cont'd

10.4 <u>Other Legislation</u>

<u>Pollution Control</u>

Drainage, noise and dust are generally dealt with under planning conditions. There are no statutory standards relating to neighbourhood noise or dust levels, although the NCB requires the consent of the water authority to discharge trade effluent into water courses and has to meet any necessary treatment costs. At least one Water Authority regards surface run-off from spoil tips as coming within this definition.

Under the Control of Pollution Act 1974, sites used for depositing controlled waste require a licence from the Waste Disposal Authority (WDA) (in England the County Council), as well as planning permission. Waste from coal mines and other mineral waste is not included in the definition of controlled waste.

Mineral wastes are often surveyed along with controlled wastes by County Councils in areas of high output, in order to seek better utilisation and co-ordination of available disposal sites and voids.

The attachment of conditions to waste disposal licences gives WDAs an extra element of control to protect public health, prevent water pollution and/or to uphold environmental standards. Prior to any licence being granted the WDA must consult with other authorities such as: Regional Water Authorities, Environmental Health Authorities, the Health and Safety Executive and (where necessary) the British Geological Survey.

A site licence controls the detailed operation of the site. However, conditions only apply for the duration of a licence which may end when disposal operations cease. Enforcement only applies to the licence holder, not the land owner. WDAs have the power to require controlled waste to be removed from where it had been deposited either without a waste disposal licence, or in breach of licence conditions.

Until now WDAs have only been responsible for identifying sites for the disposal of household and trade refuse although the Control of Pollution Act (when this section is enacted) will give them a wider responsibility for co-ordinating the disposal of all controlled wastes. Several WDAs are now drafting Waste Management Plans under the Act. These may refer to the possibility of co-disposal of major waste products whether they are controlled or mineral wastes.

<u>Derelict Land Reclamation</u>

For the most part this Research Project has been concerned with attempts to improve the decision making process for future spoil disposal rather than with reclamation processes to cope with the legacy of past dereliction. However, for completeness this subject is covered in this section.

L

10.4 cont'd

Derelict land has no statutory definition but is normally taken to mean land so damaged by industrial or other development that it is incapable of beneficial use without treatment.

Derelict Land Surveys co-ordinated by the DoE indicate the amount of derelict land justifying restoration. Colliery spoil tips constitute the largest single source in the derelict spoil tip category. Minerals surveys also identify the amount of land being used by current mineral workings. The most recent set of surveys was conducted in 1982. The Derelict Land Survey shows that there were 1,377 hectares of derelict colliery spoil tips in the Yorks, Notts, Derby coalfield at that time.

Most tips at closed collieries that predated planning conditions are handed over by NCB to local authorities under agreed reclamation programmes at a nominal cost. However, in some cases the NCB may retain certain GDO tips as tipping reserves or for coal stocking areas, or for reworking the coal content, and this delays reclamation.

Under the Derelict Land Act 1982 local authorities (either County or District Councils) are eligible for 100% DLG from the DoE on approved schemes in assisted areas and derelict land clearance areas. Elsewhere in England, 50% grants are available. Grants are available to cover not only reclamation but also towards the provision of development infrastructure such as access roads, water and sewers. The Scottish Development Agency and the Welsh Development Agency make 100% grants available to all local authorities in Scotland and Wales respectively.

DLG is also available to the non-local authority sector including the NCB. The rate of grant is 80% in assisted and derelict land clearance areas and 50% elsewhere of any net loss together with an allowance towards the costs of survey and site investigation. Because of the superior position of local authorities to obtain grants, there are few instances of reclamation by the NCB financed by DLG.

Local authorities are concerned that the capital cost of derelict land schemes will count against their capital expenditure allocations. Coalfield reclamation schemes may therefore be given lower priority in the face of competing demands on local finances. There is also concern that priority in approving schemes is now given to cases where there is greatest chance of subsequent private sector investment in developing the site for industry, housing, etc. (Ref. 27). The NCB also believes that greater priority should be given by DoE to providing DLG funds to coal mining areas and to enabling rolling programmes to be set up.

10.4 cont'd

Opencast Working

Under the 1958 Opencast Act the Department of Energy approved and authorised the working of opencast sites. Such sites were recognised as having deemed planning permission under the 1971 Town and Country Planning Act. Local authorities (both County and District Councils) were consulted and could require a Public Inquiry to be held if the application was contentious. Advocacy policies relating to the location and operation of opencast sites could be included in Structure Plans. Restoration and aftercare conditions have been attached to authorisations as standard practice.

The Government is committed to repeal relevant provisions of the Opencast Act to bring opencast workings into line with other mineral operations.

Transitional arrangements are now in place whereby responsibility for planning approval rests with the MPA and for authorisation with the DoE. The DoE will call a Public Inquiry if the application is contentious.

Private contractors wishing to work opencast sites under licence to the NCB are required to apply for planning permission in the usual way.

11.0 <u>OTHER PARTIES</u>

11.1 <u>Department of Energy</u>

The Department of Energy (DEn) is the sponsor department for the NCB. It has a number of interests with regard to spoil disposal. In particular, as the sponsor department, it is ultimately responsible for the provision of public financial assistance to the Board. The Board's operating account losses are substantial, having been over £400 m. in both 1981/82 and 1982/83 before deficit grant. The effect of the overtime ban and strike was to increase losses to £875m in 1983/84 and £2,225m in 1984/85. In addition, a large capital programme has meant that the Board's External Financing Limit (EFL) has exceeded £950m. in each of the three years to 1983/84. The EFL rose to £1,183m in 1983/84 and £1,720m in 1984/85.

Whilst the present approach to the problems of uneconomic capacity may reduce these losses, it is likely that, in the short term at least, any increase in the costs of spoil disposal will fall upon the Exchequer rather than the Board's customers. The incidence of any potential cost increases to the NCB must therefore be of concern to the Department of Energy.

Until recently, the Department was the authority which authorised and determined opencast planning applications. These duties are now in the process of being transferred to the Department of the Environment for authorisation, and to the MPAs for determination of applications.

11.2 <u>Ministry of Agriculture, Fisheries and Food</u>

MAFF's main role, in relation to proposed developments in the UK, is to seek to minimise the loss of agricultural land. Its chief concern is that agricultural land is a finite national resource, which is constantly being taken by development. The Ministry seeks to minimise the loss of agricultural land through its input into the planning system, which involves consultations with Planning Authorities on Structure Plans, Local Plans and individual applications.

Government policy for the protection of agricultural land is stated in paragraph 3 of Department of Environment Circular 75/76 (Ref. 28). It is to ensure that, as far as possible, land of a higher agricultural quality is not taken for development where land of a lower quality is available and that the amount of land taken is no greater than is reasonably required for carrying out the development in accordance with proper standards. The quality of land is measured in terms of the five grades of MAFF's Agricultural Land Classification (Grade 1 being the highest category).

In connection with spoil disposal MAFF is involved both with particular proposals and with the wider policy issues. Its main concerns are agricultural land take and quality of restoration.

11.2 cont'd

MAFF is a statutory consultee in the planning application process on applications which involve agricultural land of 10 acres or more. At the planning stage of a disposal scheme MAFF may be consulted by both the NCB and the MPAs. Procedurally, MAFF channel their comments through the MPAs and will initially advise on matters such as the quality of land to be affected, its productivity and 'fit' into farmstead structure.

Under the 1981 Minerals Act MAFF will often be asked to advise a MPA on whether a proposed site should be reclaimed to agriculture, and if so, the content of restoration and aftercare conditions. MAFF also has a role in monitoring the implementation of the aftercare conditions. Guidance on aftercare powers is contained in DoE Circular 1/82. Much of the input provided by MAFF is done by Officers of the Land and Water Service at the Ministry's Regional and Divisional Offices. It is understood that, as a result of the level of involvement and demand for their services, MAFF's labour and resources are increasingly stretched.

In the event of opposition to a particular tipping proposal, MAFF do not have formal powers to call a Public Inquiry but can influence the DoE so to do. In some cases MAFF may recommend that non-agricultural after-uses should be considered, for example where there are limited soil-forming materials or the site is likely to suffer vandalism or trespass. Taking a realistic view in such instances may help to relieve pressure on higher quality productive land elsewhere.

MAFF has a special relationship with the OE in terms of acting as its agent in the restoration process. MAFF employs and supervises a contractor to plant and manage restored sites for the five year aftercare period, all MAFF costs being reimbursed by OE.

In its wider role, MAFF is concerned to improve standards of restoration and to improve the framework for decision making on spoil disposal.

In the past, disposal options have generally not involved restoration proposals, which has resulted in the permanent loss of land and its productivity. More recent developments incorporating restoration strategies have meant that spoil heaps have been reclaimed and the land, in its new form, returned to agricultural use. Therefore, the loss of agricultural land has only been of a temporary nature although long term productivity may also be affected. The implementation of progressive restoration strategies has further reduced the length of time during which land is temporarily out of agricultural use.

Even with the advances in restoration policies and techniques now available, in MAFF's opinion the productivity of land will probably never reach the same standard as that of the original land. There is a combination of technical reasons for this which relate to factors such as the availability of soil-forming materials, the structure of re-used soils, the biological activity in soils,

11.2 cont'd

drainage, gradient and maintenance. The loss of agricultural land
may be redressed but its reduction in quality is likely to be
permanent.

Experience through monitoring restoration of opencast coal, iron-
stone and sand and gravel workings has shown the need to apply
careful husbandry practices for at least five years after restoration in order to build up soil structure and crop flexibility.
The same farmer before and after disturbance is also an advantage.
MAFF has tried to spread the principles of good practice by taking
part in NCB internal seminars on restoration.

In terms of future spoil disposal, MAFF is concerned that the
decision making process should fully take account of the finite
value of agricultural land to the nation.

MAFF is becoming increasingly concerned at the amount of
agricultural land being taken for coal mining and waste disposal
operations primarily because sites for new mines, new tips and tip
extensions are invariably on land in agricultural use. In relation
to the loss of agricultural land through other forms of development
such as housing, commerce and industry, the percentage of land
taken by coal mining is considered to be comparatively small, but
nevertheless important.

For this reason MAFF now strongly advocates the disposal of spoil
into existing voids and appreciates that in some cases this means
remote disposal. This approach reduces the need to encroach onto
agricultural land and can be advantageous to the receiving site by
way of reclaiming it and either returning it to productive (agricultural) use where there are sufficient covering soils, or
returning it to recreation which may, in turn, relieve pressure on
other good quality agricultural land. At the Vale of Belvoir
Public Inquiry, MAFF made a stand on the issue of agricultural land
take and was subsequently involved in the Remote Disposal Working
Party. The Ministry's view is, therefore, that the feasibility of
such schemes should always be explored fully before agricultural
land is used for new tips or tip extensions although MAFF itself
does not have any funds to contribute to the additional transport
costs involved. It does, however, advocate the production of
overall plans, showing the location of voids which could
potentially receive waste, throughout the U.K. This could be
compiled from survey information produced by the MPAs.

11.3 Forestry Commission

The Forestry Commission also has a role in the spoil disposal
process in terms of the advice it may give to the MPA under the
1981 Minerals Act on restoration and aftercare conditions when the
intended after-use is managed timber land. In many cases though,
planting on tips is in small amenity woodlands in which case the
Forestry Commission is not a statutory consultee but may be willing
to advise the MPA if requested. The Commission continues to be
involved in DOE sponsored research into engineering and cultivation
practices aimed to achieve high plant survival and growth rates on
re-graded spoil.

11.0 cont'd

11.4 <u>National Farmers Union</u>

The NFU's role in connection with spoil disposal is primarily to safeguard the interests of its members. In formulating views on individual tipping schemes NFU will, therefore, take a more local interest than MAFF, being more concerned with how the proposal would affect farm structure and productivity than with the formal grading of the land. NFU makes its views felt by commenting on proposals at the planning application stage. In many cases, where an existing farmer has agreed satisfactory financial terms with the NCB, there may be no NFU involvement.

The NFU does play a wider role in defending farming interests. It comments generally to planning authorities on Structure and Local Plans and sits on various liaison bodies such as the group monitoring the effects of the Selby development on drainage, and MAFF's forum on land restoration following mineral workings. The NFU was also a member of the North East Leicestershire Prospect (NELP) Remote Disposal Working Party.

The NFU has three main concerns over spoil disposal : the direct effects of land take, the indirect effects on farm prices/rentals in the vicinity of tipping schemes, and possible pollution problems on adjoining land such as from wind blown toxic dust. It should be noted that spoil disposal is only one part of the overall effect of mining on farmers; another inter-related problem is the effect of subsidence on farmland, particularly through disturbance to field drainage.

Although there is little practical experience so far of the effectiveness of restoration on colliery spoil, the NFU stresses the importance of the individual farmer to the success of the process. Careful management is needed to sustain initial yields and to build up flexibility of crop production. The NFU would like to see future research devoted to the more practical issues of restoration and monitoring results.

The NFU considers that increased attention should be given to using colliery spoil to reclaim old mineral working voids to enhance the environment and sometimes to create new farmland. Colliery spoil should also be used on top of dried out pfa lagoons to provide a better topography for farming and to improve drainage. The NFU would like to see the momentum gained by the Remote Disposal Working Party maintained, although they themselves have no money to contribute to the additional transport costs required by such schemes.

11.0 cont'd

11.5 <u>Water Authorities</u>

Water Authorities are involved in the spoil disposal process at both the planning stage and during the operational tipping stage.

When potential sites are being considered, comments from the relevant Water Authority will be sought on such issues as the presence and preventative measures necessary to protect aquifers, water courses and flood plains. The Water Authority is then a statutory consultee when a planning application is eventually submitted.

Before commencing a scheme the NCB has to obtain a 'consent to discharge' licence from the Water Authority under Section 7 of the Rivers (Prevention of Pollution) Act, 1951 and 1961. Implement-ation of Section 34 of the Control of Pollution Act 1974 is, however, underway and this Act will supersede the 1951 Act. The licence specifies the required quality of discharge by setting maximum limits allowable on the content of suspended solids and hydrocarbons. This applies to trade effluents such as arising from lagoons and is also taken by some Authorities to include run-off from coarse tips.

During the operational phases of tipping, the quality of discharge is monitored by the Water Authority which is empowered to sample the discharge and to issue penalties where appropriate.

11.6 <u>Environmental Interests</u>

Several organisations are anxious to reduce the overall environ-mental impact of spoil disposal and may make representations on individual schemes at the planning application stage. These range from Government aided organisations such as the Countryside Commission and the Nature Conservancy Council to voluntary interest groups such as the Council for the Preservation of Rural England.

The Countryside Commission's responsibilities include conserving the landscape beauty of the countryside, developing and improving facilities for informal recreation and access in the countryside and advising the Government on matters of countryside interest in England and Wales. The Commission identifies spoil disposal as a matter of significant environmental concern. In particular, the Commission wishes to see the cessation of all tipping of spoil on beaches and the restoration of damaged coastline taking place.

The Nature Conservancy Council's duties relate to conserving the natural beauty and amenity of the countryside. The Council provides advice to the NCB on the importance of nature conservation of potential tipping sites as well as sites under consideration for new mines or opencast sites.

11.6 cont'd

The Royal Commission on Environmental Pollution has also, over the years, taken an interest in waste disposal issues including spoil tipping on the Durham beaches. Its membership includes academics, politicians, representatives of industry and the workforce, and environmentalists. CENE was set up as a result of work undertaken by the Royal Commission.

Financial Review

FINANCIAL REVIEW

12.0 Costs of Spoil Disposal

12.1 Introduction

Costs can be described at three levels:

- overall cost per tonne of spoil disposed
- cost per tonne of spoil for each main activity within the spoil disposal process
- unit costs for individual components within each activity

The NCB considers only the first two indicators to be useful due to the difficulties in generalising on unit rates in circumstances where working methods and conditions vary significantly.

Unfortunately the various data sources available have estimated costs per tonne in different ways and for different purposes, making direct comparisons difficult. Three data sources are examined sequentially in this section.

The first, and most comprehensive guide, is contained in an internal NCB report by Butler and Dunn (Ref.7) produced in July 1983 and updated in 1984. This report makes projections of the differences between disposal locations: local, semi-remote (termed here for consistency on-site and local off-site) and remote.

The second source comprises the feasibility studies for the remote sites considered for the North East Leicestershire Prospect (Ref.6) and for Pyewipe (Ref.29). This work is broadly comparable with the NCB work as it was designed to show the cost differences between disposal locations.

Both these data sources present disposal costs as annual operating costs per tonne of spoil (which takes account of capital costs by way of allowances for depreciation and interest). Capital costs are also presented separately.

The third data source represents the findings of the case study programme. Although the number of schemes investigated is insufficient from which to generalise, the information is indicative of the level and composition of actual costs under different circumstances. The method of calculating costs in the case studies (the Equivalent Annual Cost [EAC]) however, differs from the annual operating cost method used in the theoretical studies in its treatment of capital costs. For this reason care must be taken in comparing the resultant costs, and also because of the difference in purpose behind the exercises; the theoretical studies sought to demonstrate the cost difference between on- and off-site tipping, whereas information for the case studies was provided to test the Evaluative Framework.

12.0 cont'd

12.2 <u>NCB Internal Study</u>

Although the Butler and Dunn study is, in part, based upon actual costs assembled on an Area basis, it uses this information as a basis for making projections of the differences between disposal locations.

For local on-site tipping these projections are based on a new theoretical tipping site of 100 hectares capable of accepting 1 million tonnes of spoil per annum for a tipping life of 25 years. The same assumptions are retained for the local off-site disposal option but the tipping site is assumed to be at a "semi-remote" location within 10 kilometres using road transport. The remote option assumes a disposal site 100 kilometres away using rail transport. All estimates are given in 1983 prices.

<u>Costs of On-site Disposal</u>

On this basis, overall costs for on-site tipping are estimated at between £1.50 and £2.50 per tonne of spoil depending on the method of fines disposal. The breakdown of these costs by activity is shown below.

<u>TABLE 12.1</u>

<u>PROJECTED COSTS OF ON-SITE TIPPING</u>

	Annual Costs per tonne of spoil	
Activity	Coarse & Lagooning	Coarse & Filter Press
Land Acquisition	0.16	0.16
Site Preparation & Fixed Plant	0.58	0.58
Treatment*	0.19	1.10
Handling & Transport	0.48	0.60
Restoration & Aftercare	0.06	0.06
TOTAL	£ 1.47	£ 2.50

Source : Butler and Dunn (Ref. 7) plus subsequent
NCB revisions

Note* Treatment costs based on assumed split of 80% coarse discard and 20% fines discard.

12.2 cont'd

Capital costs for a scheme handling 1 mtpa of spoil are estimated to be in the order of £6 to 9.5m comprising:-

	Capital Costs	
	Coarse & Lagooning	Coarse & Filter Press
Land Acquisition	£1m	£1m
Site Preparation	£1m	£1m
Fixed Plant	£2m	£2m
Mobile Plant	£1m	£1m
Lagoon Construction	£1m	-
Filter Press	-	£4.5m
TOTAL	£6m	£9.5m

Source : Butler and Dunn (Ref. 7)

Since the estimation of these costs relate to a completely new facility, they might over-estimate the costs likely to be incurred at an established colliery which may often involve the re-use of existing fixed and mobile plant.

In looking at the make up of tipping costs, the largest component of on-site costs is usually handling and transport. Costs vary according to the type of handling equipment used (conveyor and/or surface mobile plant for dry material and pipeline for wet) and the distance to the disposal point. An NCB internal survey of actual costs at Area level gave a national average of 55p per tonne for handling and transporting coarse discard. The average for individual Areas varied from about 50% below this figure where tipping is predominantly on-site (Doncaster) to 100% above this (North East) where there is a substantial element of off-site tipping, including harbour dues and marine royalties. The NCB pointed out that the actual costs found by Area were not suitable for quotation because they were said to predate more recent moves to centralise surface plant, and for some Areas did not include labour and maintenance charges.

Land Acquisition costs will vary according to the agricultural quality of the land and whether there are any mineral rights attached. Purchase prices in the range of £7,000 to £12,000 are assumed. In many cases, however, land for future tipping is already owned by the NCB. Other costs included in this category are any compensation payments to tenants and any charges for wayleaves across land not owned by the Board.

12.2 cont'd

Site Preparation costs include demolition, diversion of Public
Utilities, accommodation and civil engineering works, which will
vary with the existing state of the land and the amount of earth
moving necessary.

Restoration and aftercare costs cover final grading, replacement of
sub- and top-soil, agricultural operations leading up to cultivation and the five year maintenance period. The Butler and Dunn
exercise assumed a cost of £15,000 per hectare although MAFF
considers a figure of £10,000 per hectare is more realistic based
on their experience with opencast operations. The precise figure
will, however, vary with the surface area of any tip or backfilled
void to be treated.

Other costs that might be included in a spoil disposal scheme
include design, tip working facilities or special monitoring
measures.

No allowance for revenues was included in the NCB exercise. These
may arise when a tip is returned to an agricultural holding after
completion of the aftercare period. Practice varies as to whether
individual Areas sell the land at this stage, in which case they
might expect to get about half the value they paid for it, or rent
it as a tenancy. Any mobile plant still within its write-off
period on completion of tipping and which could be transferred to
another scheme would also count as a revenue. No return would be
expected from fixed plant; scrap values usually only cover the
costs of dismantling.

The presence of fines treatment equipment is the single biggest
variable in determining on-site tipping costs. Table 12.1 shows
the net effect of fines treatment as adding an additional £1 per
tonne to the overall cost compared to coarse tipping with lagoons.
On a tonnage basis for the fines element alone the comparative
costs of the two main disposal methods are about £1.15 for lagoons
against £4.60 to £6.50 for filter pressing, depending on cycle
times (see Table 12.2).

As can be seen both main methods require conventional thickener.
Hence, if this element is excluded the ratio of filter pressing to
lagoon costs becomes between 8 and 12:1 (£3.90 - £5.80 : £0.47 per
tonne of dry solids). This ratio differs from that provided by NCB
in a paper by Blelloch (Ref. 8) in that it attempts to make some
allowance for lagoon bank construction (NCB considering no additional costs to be involved compared to normal coarse discard
operations); and also for restoration. The ratio also differs from
the findings of CENE which gave a ratio of 2:1; this attempted to
include the full costs of lagoon bank construction and strength-
ening.

12.2 cont'd

TABLE 12.2

COMPARATIVE COSTS OF LAGOONS AND FILTER PRESSES

Component	Cost £/tonne dry solids	
	Lagoons	Filter Presses
Conventional Thickening	0.68	0.68
Piping and Pumping	0.26*	-
Filter Presses:		
1. Capital interest and Depreciation		1.6 (1 hr. cycle) to 2.86 (2. hr. cycle)
2. Operational Manpower		0.74 to 1.10
3. Maintenance		0.58 to 0.67
4. Power		0.32 to 0.51
Sub-total (1-4)		3.24 5.14
Surface Mobile Plant	0.15 (estimated)	0.60
Restoration	0.06 (estimated)	0.06 (estimated)
TOTAL	1.15	4.58 to 6.48

Source : Reproduced from Ref. (with additional detail from
Ref. 13 and Consultants' additions marked (estimated)

Note*   Figure shown is inclusive of 1. to 4. and includes the
costs of returning water back to CPP.
Costs are based on a throughput rate of 60 tonnes per
hour of dry solids (equivalent to a colliery producing
about 1M tonnes of saleable product per annum).

The costs supplied by the NCB of alternative forms of dewatering
equipment, including cement stabilisation are:

- £4.80 per tonne for solid bowl centrifuges
- £5.45 per tonne for filter belt presses
- £7.58 per tonne for deep cone thickeners.

Although the scale of difference between costs of dewatering
equipment and the use of lagoons is large for each tonne of fines
discard, the overall effect on total costs of local tipping is less
dramatic as fines average about 12½% of total spoil output at any
colliery.

12.2 cont'd

The relative proportion of capital and operating costs incurred by mechanical dewatering processes varies between the different types of dewatering equipment, cycle time, hours available for operation, method of disposal, siting and method of plant construction.

Significant capital costs can also be incurred in the construction of a new press plant building. NCB quotes current prices of about £6m for a new filter press house with a capacity of 60 tonnes per hour as the average of six bids for a recently completed project. Costs of adding a press house to an existing building are proportionately higher than provision within a new building.

A manufacturer's quote in 1985 suggested a capital cost of about £200,000 installed for filter pressing equipment of 2m x 1.5m size and 10 tonnes per hour capacity. However, the NCB states that the cost of this equipment ex-works installed together with its ancillary equipment would be in the order of £500,000.

Costs of Local Off-site Disposal

Overall costs for tipping at a semi-remote location are estimated at between £3.14 and £3.38. The components are summarised in Table 12.3. Competitive tendering may reduce these costs in practice.

TABLE 12.3

PROJECTED COSTS OF LOCAL OFF-SITE DISPOSAL

	Annual Costs per tonne of spoil	
Activity	Coarse & Fines in Suspension £	Coarse & Filter Cake £
Site Rental	0.30	0.30
Site Preparation & Fixed Plant	0.58	0.58
Treatment & Road Transport	1.66	1.90
Handling at Disposal Site	0.60	0.60
(Restoration & Aftercare) where required	(0.06)	(0.06)
TOTAL	£ 3.14	£ 3.38

Source : Butler and Dunn (Ref. 7) plus subsequent NCB revisions.

M

12.3 cont'd

It can be seen that the method of fines treatment has a much smaller effect on the total cost than in the on-site case. This is because the expense of road tankers for fines transport (£4.40 per tonne of fines discard) largely offsets the additional costs of dewatering treatment. If fines were to be transported by pipeline the cost saving would be about 66p per tonne thus reducing the total cost from £3.14 to £2.48.

Capital costs would be of a similar order of magnitude to the on-site option but reduced to exclude purchase costs of the tipping site.

The activity components making up the total costs of off-site disposal schemes remain largely of the same order of magnitude as on-site tipping except for site acquisition and the transport element. With off-site schemes the NCB is more likely to incur a rental or royalty charge rather than purchasing the site outright; revenues are therefore unlikely to occur in the same way as for schemes on NCB land. Transport costs will be the largest component for off-site schemes, increasing with distance away from the colliery.

Projected Costs of Remote Disposal

The average build-up of costs by activity for remote disposal is given in Table 12.4. It is largely based on NCB's input into the NELP Remote Disposal Working Party and reflects the costs of rail transport for 1 mtpa operation from Asfordby to the Bedfordshire Brickfields.

TABLE 12.4

PROJECTED COSTS OF REMOTE DISPOSAL

Activity	Annual Costs per tonne of spoil Coarse & Filter Cake
Site Rental	0.30
Site Preparation	0.13
Fixed despatch plant	2.70
Treatment	1.10
Rail Freight Rates	3.60
Rolling Stock	1.06
Handling at Disposal Site	0.60
Restoration and Aftercare	0.06
TOTAL	£ 9.55

Source : Butler and Dunn (Ref. 7)

12.2 cont'd

Capital costs for a 1 million tonne spoil per annum scheme are estimated to be in the order of £14m comprising:-

- £3.3m   Fixed plant at colliery;

- £4.0m   Rail wagons;

- £6.4m   Fixed plant at disposal site.

Compared to local tipping, the largest element of additional cost is obviously the transport element. In the case of rail transport there are high costs involved with loading and unloading facilities as well as with the haulage element itself.

12.3 Other Theoretical Studies

Two feasibility studies have provided estimates of the projected costs of remote disposal: those for NELP and Pyewipe. The NELP study also included an estimate of on-site tipping at £2.10 per tonne of spoil. This is towards the upper end of NCB's range in Table 12.1 reflecting the commitment to avoid lagoons in the new coalfield.

The NELP Remote Disposal Working Party, produced in October 1983, looked in detail at four remote sites (see Figure 12.1):-

- Ketton   : a Leicestershire quarry (40km);
- Fletton   : clay pits near Peterborough (60km);
- Marston Vale : Bedfordshire brickfield (120km);
- Cliffe   : chalk pits in Kent (240km).

The annual costs based on an operation of 1 million tonnes of spoil to each of the locations are given in Table 12.5. Transport costs have been separately identified but all the other activity headings have been condensed into despatch and disposal.

TABLE 12.5

PROJECTED COSTS TO NELP REMOTE DISPOSAL SITES

Site	Annual Costs per tonne of spoil					
	By Road			By Rail		
	Despatch and Disposal	Transport	Total	Despatch and Disposal	Transport	Total
		£/t			£/t	
Ketton	2.03	2.00	4.03	3.08	3.25	6.33
Fletton	2.39	3.56	5.95	2.88	3.40	6.28
Marston Vale	2.44	4.40	6.84	2.91	4.35	7.26
Cliffe	2.04	8.40	10.44	2.43	8.41	10.84

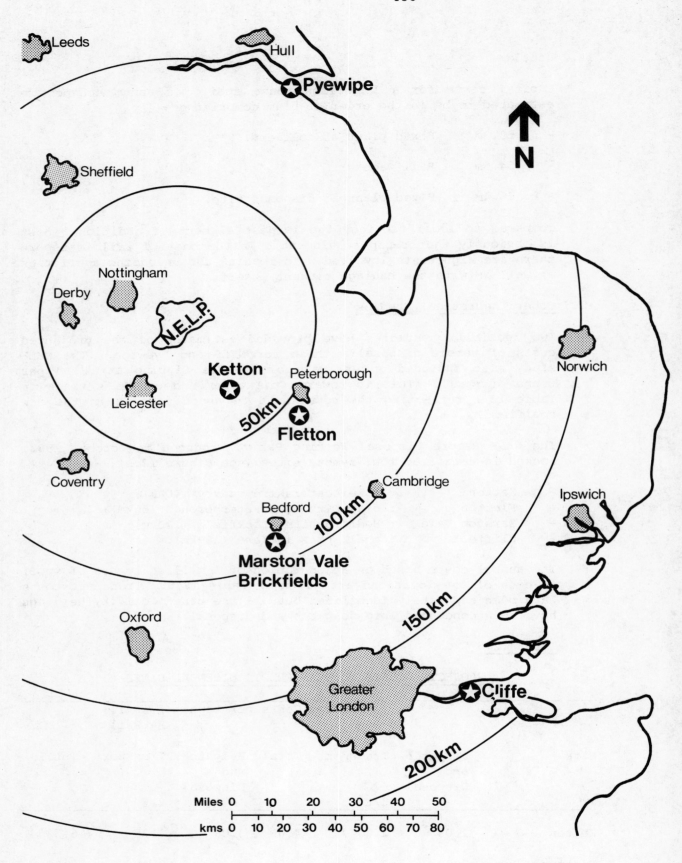

Source: Reproduced from Ref. 6

**REMOTE DISPOSAL
LOCATIONS**

FIGURE 12

12.4 cont'd

The costs of operating the despatch and disposal points on the road-borne options are broadly similar to NCB's estimated costs for on-site tipping. Rail-borne despatch and disposal is progressively more expensive. The difference between the transport element of road and rail reduces with distance. Overall cost differences between road and rail also reduce with larger volumes of spoil as seen from additional calculations assuming 2 million tonnes per annum of spoil given in the Final Report of the Remote Disposal Working Party.

For the purposes of demonstration the Report notes that remote disposal of spoil to Peterborough by rail could add between £1.00 and £1.50 to the cost of a tonne of NELP coal compared to local tipping.

The Pyewipe Study commissioned by the Strategic Conference of County Councils in Yorkshire and Humberside, gives figures in 1983/84 prices. From a number of alternatives a scheme was costed which assumed the transport of 4.2 million tonnes per annum of spoil by rail from South Kirkby and Grimethorpe to the reclamation site on the Humber Estuary for a period of 21 years. The estimated annual costs per tonne of spoil were:-

£1.14	Despatch and Disposal
£2.64	Transport
£3.78	Total.

Cost inputs to the study of alternative transport systems between collieries and to Pyewipe were contributed by NCB, BR, British Waterways Board and specialist transport firms.

As a further example the total costs of disposal at Pyewipe were estimated to be about 6% of the pithead price of coal against the NCB average of about 2%-3%, although at South Kirkby and Grimethorpe it is estimated to be less than 1%.

12.4 Case Study Findings

The case study programme provided detailed cost estimates for a variety of disposal schemes in the Central Coalfield and one in South Wales. Cost estimates for the historical schemes were provided by the NCB for the purposes of testing the Evaluative Framework. Projected costs of future schemes were largely taken from local authority feasibility reports. Most costs were expressed in 1984 prices.

The EAC method used in the case study programme is based on discounted cashflow techniques whereby all costs, including capital, are included as cash items. In general the EAC may be expected to give a slightly lower figure than the annual operating cost method.

12.4 cont'd

After allowing for the difference in methodology as well as the difference in purpose between the studies, it is still notable that the actual tipping costs indicated by the case studies are significantly lower than the level projected in the NCB internal study.

The costs of on-site tipping from six case study schemes ranged from 53 pence to £1.30 per tonne (Table 12.6). The lower end of this range represented a local tip extension incorporating lagoons. Two other local schemes had similar EACs, excluding the costs of mechanical dewatering equipment used for fines discard. The upper end of the range represented a projected estimate for a new mine facility including the cost of fines treatment and a small element (10%) of local off-site disposal.

TABLE 12.6

COSTS OF CASE STUDY SCHEMES : ON SITE

Case Study	Spoil Disposed Per Annum (million tonnes)	Method of Fines Treatment	Timescale of Scheme (Years)	Equivalent Annual Cost per Tonne of Spoil
1 (Actual)	0.37	Filter presses + Lagoons	27	£1.00
2 (Actual)	1.4	Filter presses	20	£0.55 (exc. fines treatment)
3 (Actual)	1.75	Filter presses	20	£0.60 (exc. fines treatment)
4 (Actual)	1.38	Filter presses	32	£0.72
5 (Actual)	1.2	Lagoons	11	£0.53
9 (Projected)	0.55	Filter presses	20	£1.30

In terms of the main activity components the case study findings indicate the same relative importance as the NCB internal study. The two main contributors to on-site tipping costs are handling and transport (including placement) and fines treatment where applicable. For those schemes not including the latter, handling and transport represented up to 70% of the EAC. At two collieries using filter pressing, fines treatment represented 37p out of an EAC of £1, and 20p of an EAC of 72p.

12.4 cont'd

For the other activity categories costs tended to be in the following ranges:-

- land acquisition, between 6p and 12p per tonne

- site preparation, between 8p and 27p per tonne for tipping onto agricultural land including earth moving and diversion of Public Utilities

- restoration, between 1p and 8p per tonne for existing and projected schemes respectively. Average costs would be higher where final grading and infrastructure provision for an industrial after-use is involved

- revenues, between 1p and 20p per tonne for agricultural and industrial after-uses respectively.

The costs of local off-site tipping from four case study schemes ranged from £1.66 to £1.89 excluding any costs of fines treatment. The modes of transport and distances involved are shown on Table 12.7. A fifth scheme involving restoration and infrastructure provision for an industrial after-use gave an EAC of £4.66 per tonne.

TABLE 12.7

COSTS OF CASE STUDY SCHEMES - LOCAL OFF-SITE

Case Study	Spoil Disposed Per Annum (million tonnes)	Distance to Disposal Point (km)	Mode of Transport	Timescale of Scheme (years)	Equivalent Annual Cost per Tonne of Spoil
2 (Projected)	1.4	17	Rail	20	£1.89 (exc. fines treatment)
3 (Projected)	1.75	15	Rail	20	£1.88 (exc. fines treatment)
6 (Actual)	0.2	4	Pipeline	9	£1.66 (fines only)
7 (Actual)	0.7	5	Rail	16	£1.74
8 (Projected)	0.6	14	Rail	1	£4.66 (inc. infrastructure)

12.4 cont'd

The case studies provided a useful understanding of the composition of costs within the transport element - the largest activity component for off-site schemes.

The relative importance of loading and unloading facilities as against the haulage element was shown to vary by mode, particularly between road transport and other means requiring more fixed infra-structure. For road transport the haulage element is predominant and there is a limited requirement for loading and unloading facilities. On the other hand rail, canal and also pipeline modes can involve a lot of capital expenditure on loading/unloading and emergency stockpiling areas, although in unit terms these will reduce the longer the timescale and larger the volume of spoil to be transported. Haulage costs are, by comparison, relatively less significant than in the case of road transport.

The composition of costs can also vary with the management arrange-ments adopted for a particular spoil disposal scheme. For example, surface mobile plant used in association with any of the above modes will have different cashflow patterns depending on whether the equipment is purchased or leased or whether the work is let out to contractors.

Specific points to note in relation to rail transport arising from the case studies are:-

- Loading and unloading capital costs can be at least £0.25-£0.50m depending on whether sidings are still available. Rapid loading/unloading facilities become economic to install when the expected timescales and spoil volumes are large enough. Alternatively, loading shovels can be used instead of fixed equipment where schemes are more limited. Associated labour costs will be greater with the latter than the former. Annual maintenance costs are generally estimated as a prop-ortion of the capital costs (say 5%);

- Emergency facilities would normally be necessary where spoil is being transported direct from a CPP. This would allow for stockpiling of spoil in the event of short term rail disruption or to cope with a sudden surge of production. Such facilities should generally be sufficient for about 3 days of production. Emergency facilities would not be required where spoil is to be taken from an existing tip rather than straight from the CPP;

- Wagons can either be a separate capital cost within the haulage element or be included within BR freight charges. BR have some stock available by way of old flat bottomed wagons which, although cheap to hire, involve increased discharge costs and times because of the need to grab the material out. BR are however, looking increasingly to waste scheme initiators to buy their own wagons;

12.4 cont'd

Discharging wagons can be operated more efficiently and private wagon manufacturers are currently offering competitive rates, as for example the new side tipping wagons (some of which are in use for the transfer of aggregates, agricultural lime and household refuse);

- Freight rates are estimated by BR according to the specification of a given disposal scheme in terms of tonnage per day. This is then converted into the number of trains per day (depending on size of loco and wagons) and then the required number of staff shifts.

The amount of profit then added depends on market conditions. Rates quoted for the projected case study schemes were considerably less than those in operation for existing schemes. This is because BR are keen to seek new markets in the transport of waste materials in areas where alternative tipping locations are available as well as competing transport modes. In the existing scheme included in the case study programme the transport of spoil is seen as an economic necessity through lack of alternatives and therefore part of the mineral operation. For this same reason the Area was unable to obtain any Section 8 grant towards the cost of the loading and unloading facilities.

Cancellation charges may also be included within the negotiations with BR.

From the case study work, the EAC/tonne for the transport element of rail-borne disposal schemes varied from £1.50/tonne for the existing scheme (5km) to between £1.47 and £2.06/tonne for the proposed schemes (about 15km). Freight charges accounted for up to 50% of the cashflow total in the two proposed schemes but a considerably greater proportion of the existing scheme.

The costs of remote tipping from two case studies ranged from £3.10 to £9.00 depending on distance and mode of transport (Table 12.8). Handling and transport comprised 85% of total costs at the lower end of this range increasing to 96% at the upper end.

12.4 cont'd
   TABLE 12.8

COSTS OF CASE STUDY SCHEMES - REMOTE

Case Study	Spoil Disposed Per Annum (million tonnes)	Distance to Disposal Point (km)	Mode of Transport	Timescale of Scheme (years)	Equivalent Annual Cost per Tonne of Spoil
9 (Projected)	0.55	37	Road	20	£3.10
		60	Rail	20	£4.72
		100	Rail	20	£5.80
		200	Rail	20	£9.00
10 (Projected)	4.2	144 + 88	Rail	21	£3.77 (inc. capital + interest charges)

12.5 Comparison with Mining Costs

For the NCB Areas in the central coalfield, the average cost per tonne of coal produced in 1982/83 was £37.70, although costs at colliery level varied significantly around this average. This cost is the most recent available which is not distorted by the 1983 overtime ban and subsequent strike. This cost is expressed per tonne of saleable output, the standard measure used by NCB. In general in this report, however, costs are reported per tonne of dirt disposed, a more meaningful measure when considering solely the problem of spoil disposal. In Table 6.2, the figures for spoil and saleable output indicate an average ratio of spoil to saleable output of 1 to 1.6 for the central coalfield.

Costs per tonne of spoil can therefore be converted to equivalent costs per tonne of saleable output by dividing by 1.6 (although again individual collieries will show considerable variation about this average ratio). Converting costs in this way gives the figures set out below:

12.5 cont'd

TABLE 12.9

SPOIL DISPOSAL AS A PROPORTION OF COAL MINING COSTS

Spoil Disposal Location	Cost/Tonne Spoil £	Cost/Tonne of Saleable Output £	% of Average cost at £37.70/Tonne %
On-site	1.5 - 2.5	0.9 - 1.6	2.4 - 4.2
Local Off-site	3.1 - 3.4	1.9 - 2.1	5.0 - 5.6
Remote	6 - 10	3.8 - 6.2	10.1 - 16.4

The net additional cost of remote disposal to the total costs of producing coal therefore ranges at the extreme from 7.7% (10.1 minus 2.4) to 12.2% (16.4 minus 4.2).

12.6 Comparison with Solid Waste Disposal

Existing spoil disposal costs on a per tonne basis are lower than those currently incurred by County Councils in relation to solid waste disposal. The average for all English counties in 1984-85 (excluding capital charges) across all disposal methods was £5.27 per tonne. However, several factors affect the comparison of these costs with spoil, in particular, density of material, bulkiness for transport, etc.

Table 12.10 shows the difference in costs incurred by County Councils in Metropolitan and non-Metropolitan locations. High transfer costs in the case of the GLC illustrate long distance movements such as to the Bedfordshire brickfields.

12.6 cont'd
TABLE 12.10

SOLID WASTE DISPOSAL COSTS 1984-85

	Non Metro-politan Counties (England)	Metro-politan Counties (England)	Greater London Council	All Authori-ties (England & Wales)
PRIMARY PROCESSING AND TREATMENT		£/t		
Transfer including				
- Compacting, shredding, baling	3.49	4.25	6.56	4.56
- Civic Amenity Sites	3.56	3.84	7.12	3.93
Incineration Processes	8.86	9.79	14.18	10.14
Reclamation & other methods	7.28	15.63	4.59	8.02
FINAL DISPOSAL				
Landfill direct and landfill after primary processing and treatment	1.99	2.57	2.56	2.13
Contractors, agents and other WDA's	5.23	2.83	4.40	4.28
All methods	3.85	7.27	10.51	5.27

Source : CIPFA Statistics (Ref. 11)
Note : All authorities includes England and Wales

13.0 <u>ALLOCATION OF COSTS BETWEEN PARTIES</u>

13.1 <u>Existing Cost Distribution</u>

There is little evidence to suggest that parties other than the Board are incurring any substantial direct costs as a consequence of the spoil disposal process. Most of the identifiable costs are already borne by the Board and it seems to be common practice that payments for items such as road deterioration and additional treatment are made by the Board as required. None of the MPAs consulted were able to identify significant relevant costs not presently borne by NCB.

The NCB's operating objectives are stated to include a return to profitability and a continuing reduction in real unit costs. In common with other categories of expenditure, the Board is likely to seek the minimum possible level of spoil disposal costs that will ensure compliance with these objectives.

The Board does not attempt to seek merely the lowest possible cost of producing coal, however; it also has to take into account a range of other constraints. For example, the increase in production costs necessary to produce one of the best deep mining safety records in the world is a trade-off accepted by all parties. Similarly, there are some NCB Areas which have higher disposal costs than others. For example, dewatering equipment is used more frequently in South Wales where hilly terrain restricts the use of lagoons. In South Midlands and Western Areas, there is a signif- icant amount of semi-remote tipping to quarries and other derelict land sites. The principle of seeking to minimise costs whilst at the same time accepting other constraints is therefore well established.

The Board has demonstrated its willingness to recognise that it must accept responsibility for the environmental disbenefits at new greenfield sites. Where environmental gain can be obtained at minimum additional cost, it has been prepared to bear that additional expenditure and not necessarily hold to the lowest cost alternative. The change in public attitudes towards environmental issues means that this responsibility is likely to get more burdensome. Increasingly, the Board will be forced to consider semi-remote and remote options for disposal at new sites and at existing collieries. It is to be hoped that where cost differences between options are marginal but environmental effects are marked, the Board will continue to be prepared to provide the additional funds necessary to achieve environmental gain. There is obviously a point, however, at which the NCB has to recognise operating cost constraints and beyond which it would consider cost penalties for environmental gain unreasonable especially when lower cost envir- onmentally acceptable alternatives are apparent.

13.1 cont'd

Referring to the costs and benefits of current alternative disposal options for colliery spoil, the Terms of Reference for this research project stated that "It is not yet clear whether the present distribution of costs and benefits to the different parties as implied by the various options is efficient or equitable". This project has therefore to focus on "whether some redistribution between the consumer and the national and local community would provide a more acceptable solution."

This proposition is examined by looking firstly at whether current spoil disposal practice accords with the Polluter Pays Principle (PPP) advocated by the current Government, secondly whether there are any feasible alternatives to PPP and finally, whether there is scope for limited contributions to be made by other parties in certain circumstances.

13.2 Application of the Polluter Pays Principle

The stance taken by the Government regarding pollution created by industry is generally covered under the heading of the Polluter Pays Principle. Not all impacts created necessarily cause pollution in the generally accepted sense and the term "developer" would perhaps be more appropriate. In relation to the coal industry, the clearest indication of the meaning of the principle is contained in the Government's response to CENE, the 1983 White Paper "Coal and the Environment". This stated that:

- the same environmental standards should apply to the coal industry as to other mineral operators and developers and.... the costs of meeting these standards should generally be met by the industry itself (para. 25);

- the highest standards appropriate to the circumstances should be applied to new development in the older mining areas as well as to development in new coalfields (para. 27);

- [The Government] expect the coal industry - and ultimately the coal consumer - to pay the costs of meeting the environmental standards of the day. These standards are in practice set locally, taking into account the benefits that can be achieved and the costs they impose on the industry (para. 28).

The economic arguments behind PPP are straightforward. Any developer which creates pollution should pay whatever costs are necessary to restrict that pollution to environmentally acceptable standards. These costs should be incorporated into the prices charged by the industry for its products. Consumers will gear their consumption of those products to the prices set for them and will either pay more as the costs of pollution control rise, or reduce their consumption (even to nil).

13.2 cont'd

NCB's Pricing Structure in Relation to PPP

The above argument indicates that application of PPP in the sense that cost increases as a result of improved environmental standards will rebound on coal prices, will tend to lead to a decrease in coal demand. In practice it is important to distinguish between the national application of PPP and its relevance for particular collieries.

-PPP at the National Level

The NCB produces a commodity for which there is a clearly established world market. There is competition between producers (countries) and for products (energy supply). A number of studies have indicated that imported coal could be price-competitive in the UK, particularly at coastal locations. If NCB were to increase its prices it is likely that:

- demand for NCB coal will decrease;

- imported coal (and possibly other fuels) will take a significant proportion of the drop in demand;

- NCB will be faced with the problem of excess capacity.

In an unrestricted situation, the consequence of increasing the price of coal to alleviate pollution will be to leave marginal collieries (i.e. those with the highest total units costs of production and distribution) without a market for their coal. In the long term, this excess capacity must be removed and collieries closed.

The logical consequence of PPP, as outlined above (as opposed to say subsidies for environmentally-related costs), is for a lower demand for UK produced coal and/or a rationalisation of production at collieries. The eventual trade-off may then become one between increased coal imports and lower pollution in this country but at the expense of jobs here.

-PPP at the Local Level

The NCB does not have a pricing structure which is related directly to the output of individual collieries. Prices are set differently in different markets. In the case of supplies to CEGB, for example, NCB's single biggest customer, prices are set by a formula agreed nationally which effectively bases prices in therms and not tonnes of coal. The formula allows for a number of adjustments relating to factors such as ash content. This nationally based approach does permit individual collieries to improve their revenues on a per tonne basis within clearly defined cost constraints - for example the ash content element offers an incentive to produce cleaner coal.

13.2 cont'd

Although individual collieries can influence the proceeds per tonne which they receive, it is true to say that the cost structure of an individual colliery does not, in the short run, influence the prices which can be obtained for its coal. This is because coal prices are either determined by national agreement (as in the case of the CEGB) or else they are negotiated at a regional level by the marketing department. Obviously nationally the total costs of all collieries clearly influence all coal prices (together with other factors such as the cost of inputs and competing fuels). Nevertheless, if an individual colliery were to find that its costs increased beyond its control (for example by imposed environmental standards) it would not be able to increase its revenue immediately to match. This poses the question of whether or not NCB is able to apply the polluter pays principle in practice.

Whilst at a colliery level environmental demands have to be met prior to the grant of a planning permission the NCB's pricing structure leads us to conclude that PPP does not strictly apply at local level. This is because an environmentally related increase in cost at a particular colliery would not lead to a corresponding price increase at that colliery and in turn would not trigger the PPP mechanism described earlier. We feel that the principle does apply at a broader level. However:

i)   in the long run, the Board is under a remit from Government to operate profitably. Over all its coal sales, therefore, the Board must seek to recover all its costs. This means that coal prices will be set so as to produce revenues which will meet operating costs and contribute to capital replacement. In consequence, therefore, environmentally related costs will be recovered, but only across all collieries and not at any individually. This means in effect that all consumers will share all environmentally related costs (disregarding issues such as different margins in different markets). If one colliery supplying one consumer faced a cost increase through the need to meet enhanced environmental standards, that consumer would not alone have to meet such cost increases;

ii) PPP can still be seen to work in the sense that the Board has to match supply with demand in cash terms. A significant increase in environmental costs leading to a change in the overall cost structure will change the supply/demand balance and prices will be increased and/or capacity reduced to compensate;

iii) if increased costs due to PPP were to be followed through and if the consequence were to be the closure of a colliery, in all probability the colliery which would be closed would be the greatest financial loss maker rather than the colliery which caused the pollution control cost rise in the first instance.

13.2 cont'd

-PPP and Coal Prices

It is important to retain a sense of proportion in relation to the application of PPP. The Board produces approximately 100 million tonnes of deep mined coal per year. Disposal of the majority of the spoil produced is non-contentious and to standards (historically) agreed by all parties. Even if 25% were problematic and even if the average increase in costs of spoil disposal to reduce such problems were £2 per tonne of coal (both estimates are almost certainly excessive), the increase in total costs would be £50 million per annum. If passed on to the consumer, this would represent a price increase of just over 1%, i.e. the average price of around £40 per tonne would rise to £40.40. Generally it is felt that increases of this order:

- are not within the headroom already enjoyed by coal over other fuels, particularly heavy fuel oil;

- will encourage many customers to either import coal or switch fuels.

The above approach and pricing levels assumes a cross subsidisation between collieries.

13.3 Alternatives to Polluter Pays Principle

There are a number of alternative approaches to the issue of who pays for the costs of meeting environmentally acceptable standards. PPP is one; others are:

- to allow unrestrained pollution;

- to insist that only coal which can be won to environmentally acceptable standards be extracted;

- to review the rating system;

- to insist that NCB, rather than the consumer, pays for pollution;

- to provide for some form of subsidy so that the consumer does not have to pay for the full costs of the Board meeting environmentally acceptable standards.

Unrestrained Pollution

Unrestrained pollution is nowadays socially, environmentally and politically unacceptable. Despite the continued presence of some GDO tips, NCB does not have unrestrained powers. With regard to the construction of spoil tips, the NCB conforms to rigorous health, safety and engineering standards, as laid down in various Acts and including NCB (Production) Codes and Rules - Tips 1971. Consent for new tips is only granted subject to planning constraints which embody features to ameliorate the impact on the environment. Enforcement is possible and sometimes necessary to ensure that planning conditions are fully met.

N

13.3 cont'd

Only Win "Acceptable" Coal

The Government might insist that the Board only produces coal which can be won within environmentally acceptable standards. Notwithstanding the problem of defining environmentally acceptable standards unambiguously, this option is not really a viable solution. The Board still retains the choice of spending more on environmental aspects or restricting output. As most of the instances where environmental standards are not fully met relate to older pits in high unemployment areas this course of action would cause political conflict.

NCB Pays Pollution Costs

Legislation could require the NCB, rather than the consumer, to pay the costs of meeting environmentally acceptable standards. This approach may seem attractive in that it seeks to impose costs upon the actual polluter, rather than the consumer of its products. There are a number of drawbacks, however:

- the consumer provides the raison d'etre for the Board. It seems illogical to penalise the Board rather than the consumer as the latter is the ultimate beneficiary;

- it would be almost impossible to determine a system whereby the costs of disposal were unarguably identified and then not passed on in terms of price.

The NCB is a public sector body currently making substantive losses. The effect of requiring it to absorb, but not pass on, the costs of meeting environmentally acceptable standards would be to increase its losses. This would merely indirectly add to the public purse by increasing subsidy to the industry.

These losses are covered by deficit grant or loan funding so the Treasury and ultimately the taxpayer, not NCB, foots the bill. Note that, even if the Board was operating profitably, the same effects would apply, in that the Board would repay less National Loan Fund (NLF) or provide less by way of a negative External Financing Limit (EFL).

Review Rating System

At present, NCB's rating liability is calculated nationally and then divided between Local Authorities in proportion to the volume of coal produced in each area. Rates are not therefore chargeable directly on land used for spoil tipping and in some cases of

13.3 cont'd

off-site disposal the reception authority may be outside the coal-field and receive no rate contribution from NCB at all. Were the payment of NCB rates more closely linked to disposal as well as production sites, District Councils might be more willing to contribute to environmental improvements. It is recognised though that there are many other factors that need to be taken into account in reviewing the rating system.

Pollution-Avoidance Subsidies

If the winning of coal in the UK is seen as important and if costs of meeting environmentally acceptable standards for such coal are unavoidably high, then some form of subsidy could be provided to the Board. Notwithstanding its adherence to PPP, the Government has made available limited funds for spoil disposal demonstration schemes. The first take up of these funds has been an experimental pipeline disposal scheme at Horden Colliery in the North East. NCB also contributed towards the cost of this project. A second allocation has recently been made to the Welbeck co-disposal scheme for spoil and household waste in a derelict river valley in West Yorkshire. These demonstration schemes are, however, essentially a means of demonstrating the viability of projects rather than pointing towards means of redistributing costs.

There is, however, a long list of potential parties who might be prepared to contribute to improved environmental standards by way of subsidy:

-   Department of the Environment. DoE is responsible at national level for environmental policy and one of its many current duties is the disbursement of Derelict Land Grant. These grants are to assist in restoring land previously made derelict. DoE would no doubt prefer landowners and mineral operators to avoid further dereliction arising from current operations without cost to the public purse. Nevertheless, if improving environmental standards were seen to impose an intolerable cost burden on the Board, at least in the short term, subsidies might be considered but only in tightly defined circumstances. DoE's involvement might also be necessary to encourage inter-County movements of spoil;

-   Department of Energy. D/En is the sponsor Department for the NCB. It already controls the disbursement of large sums of public money each year, primarily by way of deficit grant, various social grants and NLF drawings. If national policy were to determine that the Board should be subsidised in terms of the costs of meeting EASs, D/En could act as the disbursing agency;

-   Department of Transport. DTp could become involved in subsidising spoil disposal, primarily by way of providing Section 8 grants towards the capital cost of rail-head facilities. In addition, if it was felt desirable on national grounds to encourage rail borne remote disposal and if British

13.3 cont'd

Rail was then asked to charge lower freight rates in pursuit of such a policy, DTp would effectively be subsidising spoil disposal by virtue of the increased EFL for BR which it would have to fund. BR may, in any event, be prepared to carry spoil at virtually cost price in order to generate new business in transporting waste products;

- Mineral Planning Authorities. MPAs in areas affected by coal production might be prepared to contribute towards reducing environmental problems. Similarly, authorities with areas likely to be improved by the remote tipping of spoil (the Bedfordshire brick clay workings are an obvious example) might also be prepared to contribute to encourage such remote disposal schemes. District Councils might also contribute, particularly if positive after-uses are enabled by such reclamation;

- Ministry of Agriculture, Fisheries and Food. MAFF would be interested in safeguarding productive land around the source colliery and diverting pressure for tipping to derelict sites which, when restored, might be returned to agriculture;

- Owners/operators of the potential reception site. Their interest would vary according to whether a planning condition requiring restoration was operative on that site and the availability of other sources of fill material;

- Hauliers, either road or more likely British Rail. They might see new business opportunities in the longer distance movement of spoil. In certain cases, canal movement might be feasible in which case the British Waterways Board would have an interest;

- Water Authorities. They might see advantage in a scheme less likely to create water pollution;

- EEC. EEC funds may be forthcoming for feasibility studies to test innovative remote disposal options and, in some cases, as a contribution to their implementation.

13.4 Scope for Redistribution of Costs

Although the application of PPP is generally being met with regard to colliery spoil disposal, there are circumstances where opportunities for redistribution of costs between parties may arise. These are:

- where the Board is encouraged to adopt a solution which is more expensive than another alternative acceptable on environmental grounds;

13.4 cont'd

- where significant enhancements in environmental standards are imposed.

Choosing a Higher-cost Alternative

There are cases where the Board has been encouraged by Planning Authorities to choose a spoil disposal option whose costs are greater than an option which is itself acceptable on environmental grounds. Where these additional costs to the Board are not significant it has adopted the more expensive scheme.

An example of where a higher cost option off-site is being promoted but where no agreement has yet been reached on who should bear the additional costs is the Pyewipe scheme presently under discussion to utilise NCB spoil in a major reclamation project in the Humber estuary.

The problem in such schemes is defining a formula for cost-sharing acceptable to all participating parties. There is no clearly established basis for dictating how such costs should be shared and all parties would no doubt wish to minimise the additional costs on them whilst maximising any environmental benefits. It is therefore difficult to envisage a formula which is universally applicable and which would not be controversial to at least some of the potential participants.

Each scheme will need to be treated on its merits, bearing in mind that:

- the planning system, through conditions imposed by Planning Authorities, should seek to minimise the extra costs to be imposed;

- owners of sites which are environmentally sub-standard should not expect to levy tipping royalties when such tipping will lead to environmental improvement;

- any subsidy for additional costs could have an effect on enhancing the "value" of voids by increasing their marketability;

- several other EEC countries give grants of one form or another to encourage pollution control. A recent study for DoE by Environmental Resources Limited identified several such grants, but noted that the generous capital allowances in the U.K. provided some offset. Capital allowances are not usually available to organisations not paying tax, however, and are in any event being phased out over the next 3 years;

- beneficiaries from any scheme should bear a proportion of the additional costs involved;

13.4 cont'd

- if there were any income derived from the disposal of spoil, (e.g. the purchase of bulk fill material) that income should accrue to the participants who are meeting the additional costs rather than to the NCB. Alternatively, the income could be used by the Board to offset the transport costs. There are schemes, such as Welbeck, where remote disposal clearly offers revenues as well as imposing costs. Such revenues should be used to offset the additional costs involved.

In practice, cases may arise where local circumstances force MPAs in particular to consider subsidy, for example:

- where the Board cannot meet environmentally acceptable standards and would prefer closure, but where such closure would have a significant impact on local employment;

- where intense off-site dereliction would be removed partly as a result of spoil tipping (e.g. Welbeck co-disposal scheme).

In most circumstances, however, parties other than the NCB are likely to recognise constraints upon the resources available to them and therefore argue for PPP rather than agreeing to some form of subsidy.

Rising Environmental Expectations

Environmental standards change over time. Safety was no doubt the primary reason for the changes which have taken place in spoil disposal operations since the late 1960s, but increasing environmental concern is also evident. This is reflected by conditions imposed by Planning Consents. Whereas local authority planning permissions typically had only a few conditions attached twenty years ago, today 30 or more are not uncommon.

Environmental standards involve subjective judgements, not only of the impact of a proposal on differing elements in the environmental mix, but also on the interplay between different elements. Whilst it is therefore possible to say that imposed standards are generally becoming more stringent, it is not easy to define precisely where they are at a given point in time, nor how they might change in the future.

In broad terms, the general trend of improving environmental standards comes under the Cmnd 8877 (Ref. 2) principle of "meeting the environmental standards of the day" (para. 28). There are cases where abrupt change may be imposed, however. An obvious example would be legislation which either gave local authorities more direct powers over spoil disposal generally, or laid down standards, significantly above those currently accepted, which the industry would have to meet in the future.

13.4 cont'd

There is general definition of the liability for payment of increased costs arising from legislative changes but there are some general points that can be made:

-   Government is unlikely to pay any increased cost burden as a result of its legislation;

-   legislation which does impose increased costs often has:

    .   a lengthy phasing-in period (e.g. car seat belts, exhaust emission standards)

    and/or

    .   exemptions applying to existing facilities (e.g. most town and country planning regulations);

-   sometimes a distinction might be made between the costs of meeting minimum acceptable standards, for which the operator alone is responsible, and the extra costs of going some way beyond those standards, for which some assistance may be available.

There may be a case, therefore, for transitional assistance probably from national Government, if standards were raised and the Board had difficulty in complying in the short term without incurring significant cost penalties. The DoE might also agree as a matter of principle to meet a designated proportion of the costs of schemes designed to raise environmental standards, provided that co-operative arrangements between other parties (probably the NCB and MPA) were made to find the balance of funds required.

There are a number of difficulties in carrying forward the subsidy argument in either of the two circumstances described above:

-   how can the amount to be provided by way of subsidy be identified?

-   how can schemes to be subsidised be identified?

-   why should any of the parties listed above be prepared to subsidise when they would almost certainly prefer application of PPP?

-   how to stop the arrangement providing a precedent for other extractive industries?

This study does not offer a prescriptive formula for assessing the nature and extent of subsidies, either at local or national level. Each scheme needs to be faced on its merits. It is to be hoped though, that use of the Evaluative Framework will clarify the costs of alternatives in a relatively unambiguous manner and hence reduce areas for dispute and debate.

ENVIRONMENTAL REVIEW

14.0 ENVIRONMENTAL EFFECTS OF SPOIL DISPOSAL

14.1 Nature of Impacts

Unlike the estimation of costs, there are no easy ways of measuring the environmental effects of spoil disposal schemes. The overall assessment is largely subjective even though it is possible to break the effects down into major categories and then to quantify some elements within each category. Another complicating factor is that the environmental consciousness of communities changes over time; what was once accepted as a fact of life may now be seen as an environmental problem.

In small closed communities which depended almost entirely upon coal mining for their existence, largely untreated spoil heaps were part of the general environment and accepted as a by-product of employment. However, rising environmental expectations over the last decade in particular have been reflected by the formation of Environmental Pressure Groups and growing demands for Environmental Impact Assessments (EIAs) to be carried out on major projects. It is, therefore, in this context that the impact upon the environment of spoil disposal must be viewed.

Clearly, commercial utilisation of spoil is to be preferred in environmental terms to disposal. Unfortunately, only about 1% of annual spoil output finds its way to a commercial market.

The environmental effects of a spoil disposal scheme vary with the:

- form of disposal (surface tipping, lagooning, backfilling of voids, marine disposal) and

- type of surroundings (existing colliery/mineral site or farmland, landscape quality, proximity to settlements, presence of any special features).

There are no inherent differences in the form of impact between an on-site scheme and an off-site scheme apart from the effects along the transport route with the latter. Disposal method and the environs of the site are more important and the effect of these is examined below under a description of each of the main types of potential impact. It should be noted that the type of effect will differ throughout the life of a disposal scheme. Some will be temporary effects and others permanent. Not all impacts are disadvantageous; some schemes for example may give rise to beneficial after-uses.

The impacts of a disposal scheme are also likely to be perceived differently by different interest groups. Local residents around the colliery or disposal site and along any transport route are likely to bear the brunt of most impacts during the operational stages, particularly any visual disruption, noise and dust nuisance. Occasional recreational users may also find footpaths diverted, views marred or special features disturbed.

14.1 cont'd

The impact on the landowner or tenant will differ depending on the previous use of the land. In the case of farmland the previous farmer will have received compensation in the form of payment for land but may still be able to continue activity if a viable holding remains or can be arranged through land swaps. National agricultural interests must also be taken into account as these may be affected differently from those of individual landowners or tenants. In the case of old mineral workings the landowner may benefit either financially or in terms of fulfilling a restoration obligation. In this instance the community as a whole also gains through the creation of new land with potential for a positive after-use. The wider community would also suffer if there was any water pollution from a scheme in the longer term although this risk should be capable of being guarded against.

People travelling through an area affected by a disposal scheme may experience direct effects such as delay if spoil is being taken off-site, or less direct effects such as changed views. Finally, potential investors in an area's economy may be deterred by the psychological impression of spoil heaps, particularly if left unrestored.

In judging the severity of such effects on different parties, weight would normally be given to those experiencing the effects continuously over long periods and to whom no compensation would be given.

14.2 Categories of Environmental Impact

The environmental effects of spoil disposal schemes can be grouped into five main categories:

- visual

- land use

- ecological/heritage/recreational

- pollutants

- transport route.

The first two of these impacts are virtually certain to occur with any scheme although their severity will vary with disposal method and surroundings. There are ways of ameliorating impacts, particularly in the visual category, which may marginally add to the scheme costs but would make the scheme more acceptable to the community.

14.2 cont'd

The third category will only occur when special features exist in the locality and again sensitive treatment may help to reduce the impact. The fourth category should only represent a risk of pollution rather than a positive impact. The risk should be capable of being minimised by good design and operating procedures.

Traffic impact, the last category, will only occur if the disposal site is located away from the originating colliery. The severity of impact will vary by transport mode and route.

Each of the categories is examined in more detail below.

Visual

Most would consider that colliery spoil, like any other waste material, is unpleasant visually. Its dark colour adds to this effect. It follows therefore, that the creation of tips above ground will almost always create more visual disturbance than backfilling of voids.

Nuisance experienced by local residents and other property owners will be a subjective reaction to the appearance and form of the advancing tip and the degree of loss experienced by the new land-form blocking out any previous views. In some cases the oper-ational phases of disposal may be visually intrusive but the final form and use after restoration may be acceptable. Any delays to restoration such as may occur if an old tip is retained for possible reworking of its coal content will extend the length and severity of visual nuisance.

Tips in areas of high landscape quality will generally be more controversial than in areas of lesser quality although they may be most noticeable in flat areas. Similarly the introduction of tips into new greenfield locations will generally raise more objections than in areas with a legacy of tipping. However, it must be remembered that in areas intensively covered by spoil tips, such as in the Aire and Calder Valleys in West Yorkshire, the value placed on the few remaining areas of open farmland by the local residents may be as high as those in more favoured locations.

Nevertheless, the design of a tip can do much to lessen its impact within its surroundings. Modern tips are generally designed to shallower side slopes than historically, for stability as well as environmental reasons. Nevertheless, steeper slopes are used in areas of hilly topography such as Derbyshire and breaks of slope or valley features are sometimes introduced to add interest to a tip. This is to be encouraged to move away from artificial "whale-back" shaped tips. Early restoration to grass or woodland also helps to soften visual impact.

14.2 cont'd

The area of land within which a spoil tip can be seen, sometimes
called the Visual Envelope Map (VEM), will vary with topography.
In the case study programme VEMs varied from a radius of a few
kilometres to over 20 when the site was on the edge of an exposed
ridge. VEMs may extend in all directions around a site when on a
plain or in a valley, or only in certain directions when on a
slope. VEMs can be drawn through a combination of site and map
work, or generated by computer (see Section 4.3, Procedural
Manual).

The effect of spoil tipping will usually be worse the nearer the
observer is to the disposal site. Hence the more properties
immediately adjacent, the greater the level of likely disturbance
and objection. This is not always the case since some sites may be
effectively screened by the local landform but still be highly
visible to properties slightly further away. Where local properties are sensitive, methods of working can often be adopted to
provide an early screening bank (either temporary as top- or
sub-soil or permanently as spoil) so that later workings can
progress away from the houses behind the bank. Unfortunately, this
practice is not uniform.

Some commentators, including CENE, consider lagooning to be much
more intrusive than the tipping of dry waste. However in that
lagoons are normally within the body of the tip, the visual impact
is reduced because they cannot be seen easily unless one is looking
down on the lagoon from a much higher landform, which is rare.
Also, the impact of operations can be reduced by screening using
vegetation or trees on banks. These temporary measures allow
lagoon tips to blend more easily to existing landscape before final
overtipping is carried out. On the other hand, any subsequent
raising of lagoon banks reintroduces unrestored land above that
which is greened and can result in damage to the restored lower
slopes. Where fines treatment equipment is used these risks do not
occur, although the presence of dewatering equipment itself, housed
in or adjacent to the CPP, increases the massing of colliery
buildings sometimes with visual consequences.

Backfilling of voids is generally less visually intrusive than
surface tipping because the material and associated plant are less
visible. The previous landform may or may not have been an
eyesore. Voids may be effectively screened from any local
properties such that they are only visible from further away if at
all depending on topography. The final landform, either flush with
ground level or slightly raised, is also unlikely to be disturbing.

Beach tipping on the other hand raises strong emotions because of
the associations normally made with the seaside. The legacy of
beach tipping is restricted in England to a stretch of the Durham
coastline and measures are currently being taken to concentrate
tipping at fewer outlets and clean up the back terraces along the
remaining shoreline.

14.2 cont'd

Land Use

Over 7,000 hectares nationally had been used for colliery spoil tipping by April 1974 with a further 2,200 hectares permitted for future tipping. The NCB estimates that the current use of new land for spoil tipping amounts on average to about 200 hectares per year nationally. Locally the average land take might be in the order of 3 to 4 hectares each year for a colliery with an annual output of about 1 million tonnes. The implications of land take on this scale depends on the type of land use that spoil disposal displaces.

Most surface tipping takes place on agricultural land. The severity of impact depends largely on its inherent potential. Although spoil disposal is only a temporary use, the quality of any restored land will be lower and less productive than the original land. The loss of any higher grade land is therefore of concern to MAFF. Of the twelve case study schemes only one involved Grade II land on the magnesium limestone belt through South Yorkshire.

An important effect to the particular landowner or tenant is the viability of the remaining farm holding. This depends on whether there is sufficient land remaining free from tipping at any one time during the phasing timetable and whether the parcels of land are not unduly severed from the centre of activity. Loss of crop yield over the lifespan of the tipping scheme is difficult to assess and of less overall importance than the loss of land potential.

Progressive restoration (i.e. using soil stripped at the advancing tip face for placement on the completed tip behind) is the best method of minimising agricultural land take. Its use has been effectively demonstrated in association with the stacker spreader handling system in the NCB Barnsley Area. At the other end of the scale delays in restoration or the need to reopen tips to rework their coal content or to extract opencast coal from under them, may occasionally dramatically extend the timescale over which land is out of productive use.

The use of lagoons may impede progressive restoration and involve more land out of agricultural use at any one time, as described in Chapter 8, although lagoons have little or no effect on the ability of land to regain its former potential. Where insufficient coarse material is available for overtipping lagoons, final design slopes will not be achieved leading to delays in commencing restoration. A major example of this is in the Aire Valley in West Yorkshire, where there has been extensive environmental intrusion for many years.

By contrast, backfilling of voids may have beneficial land use effects. There may have been no meaningful previous use in the case of old mineral workings. In this case and also with current workings, colliery spoil may also allow restoration to take place faster than otherwise expected and allow the land to be returned to a positive after-use. Even where this after-use is not directly to agriculture it may have beneficial effects by diverting pressure for development away from undisturbed higher grade land.

14.2 cont'd

Sea-based disposal, although restricted to three main dumping
grounds off the North East coast, has significant implications on
fisheries interests. When spoil is dumped it builds up on the sea
bed killing off vegetation and fish life. Particles held in the
water filter out light and thus prevent fish living in the upper
layers as well. Fines discard is not allowed to be dumped under
current licence arrangements. The position of these prescribed
dumping grounds was originally selected due to the absence of
significant fisheries interests and of strong currents which could
spread the effects. No additional grounds are likely to be
licenced following the Oslo Convention.

Ecological/Heritage/Recreational

Features which might be adversely affected either temporarily or
permanently under this heading are:

-   Sites of Special Scientific Interest (SSSIs), nature reserves
    or other ecological features of interest;

-   Conservation areas, listed buildings, historic ruins or other
    man-made features of importance;

-   Definitive footpaths, bridleways or other rights of way;

-   Public Open Space, school playing fields or parks.

The potential effects of any kind of disposal scheme can be direct
in terms of destruction or demolition, or indirect in terms of
detracting from their setting or polluting them. The severity of
impact will depend on the sensitivity of the habitat or feature,
whether it is re-creatible, and the extent to which it is visited
or used.

From the case study programme footpaths appear to be the most
frequent feature affected by surface tipping. The proposed diversion of a footpath can sometimes be a source of controversy with
local residents even when ultimate reinstatement to its original
location is proposed. Where the right of way has historical
significance the opposition can be particularly strong.

There may be a greater likelihood of affecting a SSSI when filling
a void than when tipping on farmland. Wilderness conditions may
have developed in old workings or on otherwise derelict sites away
from the influence of modern agricultural fertilisers. Features of
geological interest may also have been exposed in old quarries.
Sometimes such features may be able to be preserved in theory by
designing tipping phases around them but their setting and public
accessibility is likely to be lost or reduced.

14.2 cont'd

Beach tipping destroys the habitat of the foreshore and in addition material washed into the sea destroys plant and animal life in the inshore areas.

Water/Noise/Air

Any disposal scheme can cause an associated risk of pollution in each of these areas. In theory the risk should be capable of reduction to near zero with good operating procedures.

The main sources of potential water pollution from surface tips are surface water run-off and leachate. These can affect surrounding ground conditions, water courses and aquifers in terms of salinity, pH and toxicity levels. The presence of permeable bedrock requires preventative measures to be taken such as waterproofing the base (for example by membranes or puddled clay). In some situations laying an aerated medium such as gravel or clinker in the base may improve the quality of the leachate. Preventative measures need to be even more stringent in the vicinity of underlying aquifers whatever the permeability of the base. Provisions of the EEC Groundwater Directive 1980 apply to most aquifers even if they are not developed for water supply.

Seepage risks apply equally to lagooning and filling voids while surface run-off does not. Preventative measures in terms of lining the base of voids are taken in the same way as with surface tipping. In the case of lagoons a layer of coarse discard is compacted on the floor of the lagoon to reduce the downward migration of water. Monitoring is necessary for all disposal sites to control discharge to water courses or underground water.

Air pollution from disposal sites can result from dust, usually related to the transport and handling of spoil in dry conditions, or from related machinery emissions. Settlements on the down side of the prevailing wind and in certain topographical conditions are at risk. Risks are even greater from surface tipping than filling of voids, and can be reduced by controlling vehicle emissions and spraying haul roads in the summer. The risk does not apply to lagooning.

Noise pollution can result from surface plant. Its severity will depend on the proximity of the nearest settlements particularly downwind. Risks are again greater from surface tipping than voids particularly where dump trucks are used to transport spoil from the CPP rather than conveyors. The stacker spreader system is reputed to reduce noise nuisance even further. The effects on local residents can be reduced by controlling the operating hours of a site and vehicle emission levels. Once the retaining banks have been constructed there is no further noise risk with lagooning.

14.2 cont'd

Transport Route

This effect is only experienced when the reception site is located off-site from the colliery. Effects such as noise and dust nuisance caused by internal haul roads are assumed to be covered under the previous headings. Spoil is likely to be transported on the public network by road, rail or canal, or by dedicated pipe-line. The incidence of off-site transport is more likely to be associated with the filling of a void or other reclamation site with either coarse discard or wet fines than with surface tipping.

Environmental problems associated with transporting spoil are usually significantly greater with road transport than by the other modes. The quantities of spoil requiring daily transport from a colliery will result in a large number of truck trips per day. For example a case study scheme of only 0.6 million tonnes a year required in the region of 100 truck loads of 20 tonnes each per day; almost one truck every 5 minutes during the working day. If the route from the colliery to the tip passes through residential or shopping areas the additional danger and general nuisance, in terms of noise, vibration and dust, may well be a serious environmental problem for the residents. Conflict with other road traffic along the route is also an additional disadvantage of frequent truck movements.

Transporting spoil by rail takes advantage of the high capacity of rail with only a small number of train loads a day required to remove spoil from a colliery or group of collieries. Loading and unloading procedures generate extra noise (compared with road transport) due to the shunting of wagons in the sidings, but otherwise there is little difference in noise generation between loading methods. Fixed hopper arrangements would generally be quieter than loading/unloading by shovel or grab. Apart from the extra train movements along the line (which may have implications for road traffic at level crossings), there may be dust blowing off the unsheeted wagons onto adjacent land, gardens or buildings. The provision of new railway sidings or reinstatement of former sidings at the colliery or disposal site would usually be the only new construction and land take effects of a rail transport scheme.

For canal transport spoil may have to be taken off-site to the nearest canal wharf, along a fixed track (conveyor or rail) or by truck. The impacts from these facilities at either end of the canal route are likely to be the main environmental effects, together with the noise and dust effects of unloading barges if grabs have to be used. Barge movements themselves, regardless of the scale of vessel used, are unlikely to cause any noise or dust nuisance to properties on route.

New pipelines may cause severance if laid above ground but it would be expected that most would be buried. Clarification and return of water at the point of discharge would also usually be required.

o

14.2 cont'd

Other

Safety is an obvious example of another form of environmental risk. The safety of tipping sites can be considered under various headings including:

- slope stability

- risks to trespassers

- overtipping of lagoons (capping with coarse discard).

Under the Mines & Quarries (Tips) Act 1969 tips are required to be made and kept secure. The Board's Codes and Rules for Tips require a factor of safety of 1.5 for slope stability no matter what type of disposal system is employed. In fact, modern tips are generally required by planning permissions to be much flatter than would be necessitated by stability considerations.

CENE found that in the public's mind the greatest safety risk was considered to be falling into a lagoon. The Board's safety statistics, however, show no accidents involving lagoons over the three years prior to June 1985. Standing Instructions require the Board to fence off lagoons where necessary and to place warning notices to reduce risk to trespassers (Ref. 8).

Overtipping of lagoons can be carried out in a controlled manner, economically, safely and expeditiously. The recommended method of overtipping is to use a light bulldozer advancing a coarse discard layer of about 1 metre thick. Once the thickness of overtip is uniformly 2 to 3 metres it can carry a loaded scraper without risk of any person or machine breaking through to the lagoon deposits (Refs. 8 and 22).

15.0 ENVIRONMENTAL STANDARDS

15.1 Setting and Maintaining Environmental Standards

As discussed in the previous section, spoil disposal schemes impose a variety of environmental impacts some of which can be ameliorated or reduced to a minimum risk by the adoption of sensitive design and phasing. This section discusses how effective existing procedures are in coping with rising environmental expectations.

Direct Means

The NCB sees itself as adopting a responsible attitude to the environment by the maintenance of good working practices. It will properly bear the costs of restoration of current spoil disposal to existing environmentally acceptable standards. It considers it has a duty to set a high standard of environmental practice as a nationalised industry.

In addition to self regulation the NCB is also encouraged to maintain environmental standards by imposition and enforcement of planning conditions attached to the grant of planning permissions. Other bodies, such as District Councils, the Water Authorities, and the Ministry of Agriculture, Fisheries and Foods (MAFF), also have a chance to influence this process through the statutory consultation procedure carried out by MPAs on each application. Conditions on spoil disposal permissions generally seek:-

- to define the area and time period of operations;

- to identify by way of schemes/plans the stages of the tipping operation leading to the final land form and the restoration stages necessary to achieve an agreed after use;

- to seek certain safeguards on the manner of working to minimise environmental nuisance;

- to provide contingency arrangements for the satisfactory restoration of the site should circumstances change.

Conditions should not duplicate the controls of other bodies, such as Water Authorities, unless these controls cannot be relied upon separately to secure planning objectives.

Reliance on conditions attached to planning permissions to set environmental standards means that there are few controls on tipping which takes place under the GDO (as described in Section 10.2). This gives rise particularly to problems over restoration responsibilities. The NCB believes it inappropriate that it should bear the cost of inherited coalfield dereliction; instead it sees this as a matter for Derelict Land Grant.

15.1 cont'd

Where standards have been set by conditions, MPAs have a duty to monitor compliance with them. If conditions are not being adhered to, MPAs try to resolve the situation through established liaison arrangements with the NCB but, as a last resort, may take enforcement action. This means serving an enforcement notice specifying the nature of the breach, the means of putting it right and the time given to do so. A stop notice can then be served if the situation warrants it (unlikely with NCB operations). If the enforcement or stop notice is not complied with, the NCB (as with any other mineral operator) can be taken to the Magistrates' Court, where a fine may be imposed, unless the NCB appeals in which case an Inquiry will be convened.

In practice MPAs are often loathe to initiate enforcement proceedings which may damage working relationships with the NCB. During the Consultants' review only one authority in the Central Coalfield had recently considered taking enforcement action against the NCB. Use of stop notices also carries compensation implications.

Indirect Means

Indirect means by which environmental standards are set include existing informal liaison arrangements between the NCB and MPAs. These vary between NCB Areas and County Councils but in many cases seek a constructive dialogue at the pre-planning application stage. MPAs may often be able to offer specialist advice to improve the design of schemes, particularly in terms of landscaping and tree planting. MPAs can give the NCB an indication of those aspects of a scheme likely to be critical to Members, as decision makers, and suggest ways of overcoming potential problems. Some solutions, for example an NCB contribution to off-site planting, may be included in a subsequent Section 52 Agreement where it would not be a suitable subject for a condition. The NCB is prepared to attend meetings organised by Parish, District or County Councils to explain any controversial proposals. It will rarely initiate public meetings itself though and therefore may not always be aware of the strength of environmental concerns from local residents.

A further indirect means by which standards are set is as a feedback from previous permissions. The NCB will be cognisant of what conditions were previously required by a particular MPA, and by other MPAs throughout the country through its headquarter's monitoring process, and will attempt to ameliorate these concerns in its tip designs. Public Inquiries, by encouraging an open debate, also influence the setting of standards and may lead to general expectations of higher standards in the determination of subsequent applications of a similar nature in other parts of the country.

15.0 cont'd

15.2 Updating Environmental Standards

Legislative Means

The types of conditions imposed on planning permissions have obviously become more stringent over the years as environmental expectations and standards have increased. The NCB maintains that the number of conditions has also been rising rapidly in recent years although this by itself is not a reliable indicator of the level of control being imposed, as practice varies between MPAs on the separation of conditions on a similar theme.

The NCB is clearly concerned about the increasing stringency of planning conditions although has so far managed to settle its differences with the MPAs through advance negotiation rather than formally appealing against conditions imposed. The Board is concerned that conditions are increasingly straying into its area of operational expertise such as choice of earth moving vehicles. There is also some aggravation of what it perceives to be a duplication between planning conditions and controls exerted by other bodies such as Water Authorities.

Conditions are imposed according to the prevailing standards of design and environmental protection at that time. In general more onerous conditions cannot be imposed retrospectively without the MPA paying full compensation to the developer, in this case the NCB. However, MPAs have been given some new powers by the Minerals Act 1981 to review minerals sites, including spoil tips, within their counties and to modify permissions or place conditions where no permissions had previously existed. Compensation is still payable in the event of exercising these powers although draft scales for NCB operations have not yet been published.

Even though it is difficult at present to formally modify conditions over time, there is limited opportunity for the NCB and MPAs to review working practice as a large scheme progresses. Permission may be given for a site lasting 20 years or more, together with an outline design, but it is common practice for the NCB to submit detailed design and restoration proposals for individual phases to be agreed by the MPA successively throughout the scheme.

In respect of GDO tips, MPAs now have the power to ask the NCB to submit tipping schemes for any post 1974 tipping as described in Chapter 10. Experience in practice has been mixed although West Yorkshire County Council are now understood to have approved three schemes.

Another method by which environmental standards might be updated is the use of phased planning permissions. This device has been introduced into two recent spoil disposal permissions at South Kirkby and Asfordby. These have required consideration to be given to remote disposal options before starting on subsequent stages of local tipping.

15.2 cont'd

Persuasive Means

The provision of DoE funds for spoil disposal demonstration schemes
is designed to illustrate a range of innovative solutions for spoil
disposal which have the potential for improving environmental
standards. The production of the Evaluative Framework within this
Research Project, aimed at improving the site selection process for
future spoil disposal schemes, is also part of this process of
encouraging higher standards.

The NCB itself, is helping to raise environmental standards by the
dissemination of advice on good practice and the provision of
central advice at headquarters such as Environment Sections within
the Operational Research Executive (ORE) and the Civil Engineering
department. Safety standards are continually under review within
the Board and sometimes improvements here have environmental
spin-offs. For example, changes in tip design to improve stability
factors after the Aberfan distaster gave widespread advantages of
less steep side slopes.

15.3 Scope for Improving Arrangements

Effectiveness of Existing Arrangements

The setting of environmental standards locally by means of
conditions on planning permissions is effective in general terms as
long as conditions are adhered to, which is mostly the case at
present. There are, however, two main problem areas.

The first relates to the lack of control over GDO tips. The extent
of the problem has been reduced through the willingness of the NCB
to forfeit its rights when applying for new permissions on
adjoining land. Nevertheless there appears to be a residual
problem in West Yorkshire where the negotiation of tipping schemes
on behalf of both MPA and NCB has so far failed to improve the GDO
tips to any significant degree.

The second relates to the problem of updating environmental
standards, which is difficult when conditions are largely fixed for
the life of the planning permission. Because spoil tipping can
extend on any one site for more than 20 years there is an inherent
problem of the effectiveness of planning control relating to rising
environmental standards over time. Conditions attached to tips
approved in the 1960s, which were appropriate at the time of
consent, may now be considered, by planning officers and the
general public, to be too lenient. Although conditions currently
imposed are far more stringent these, in turn, may be viewed as
being too lax at some future date. Legislative changes via the
Minerals Act 1981, which are currently in the pipeline, may assist
but these are slow in being finalised. In the meantime various
attempts at persuasion are the only means of achieving increased
environmental consciousness. Again the advantages are felt mainly
in the design of new schemes, especially in new greenfield
locations, rather than through improvements to existing practice.

15.3 cont'd

<u>Alternative Arrangements</u>

Colliery spoil is not included within the definition of controlled waste under the Control of Pollution Act (COPA) 1984. Spoil disposal sites do not therefore require a waste disposal licence from the Disposal Authority.

It is worth considering here whether there would be any advantages in colliery spoil becoming a controlled waste in the same way as pulverised fuel ash deposited by the CEGB. Environmental benefits of NCB operating under a waste disposal licence system appear to be that:

-   conditions could be imposed on all tipping sites including those operating under the GDO. In the latter case such conditions could theoretically include those aspects normally covered by planning conditions although in practice such imposition is rare as applicants can appeal against waste disposal licence conditions to the Secretary of State;

-   licence conditions could be updated if the Waste Disposal Authority considered this desirable and it would not result in unreasonable expenditure by the licence holder. This therefore caters in part with the problem of rising expectations;

-   additional controls could be placed on NCB operations through licence conditions to cover:
    .   better site supervision including an office and record keeping of materials coming onto the site;
    .   better site management including general appearance, tidiness and screening;
    .   better information provision to the Authority on cessation of operations and recommencement;

-   licence conditions could be enforced more speedily as there is quicker recourse to the Magistrates' Court under COPA than under planning legislation. In practice Authorities would be equally loathe to use such proceedings against the NCB for fear of damaging relationships.

The main advantages of COPA controls being applied to the NCB would be to allow some additional aspects of site management to be controlled and to allow some updating of conditions. Examples of such improvements might be updating plans of working and modifying equipment as new anti-pollution measures become available.

A major disadvantage of the NCB having to operate under a waste disposal licence system would be the degree of overlap with existing planning conditions. This has already given cause for concern in other parts of the minerals industry and current practice is under consideration by local government officers.
There is also the possibility that the onus of finding licensed disposal sites might fall more onto County Councils if colliery spoil became a controlled waste. The NCB could also be expected to resist more controls over all its tipping sites, whether or not they were perceived to be causing environmental problems.

15.3 cont'd

COPA controls would also be ineffective in dealing with restoration issues, one of the major concerns with tipping schemes. This is because disposal licence conditions operate only for the duration of the licence unlike planning permissions which attach to the land. Thus, restoration which does not always take place concurrently with waste disposal activities cannot be controlled by the site licence.

On balance it seems to be within the NCB's power and interests in many cases to improve environmental standards in quite small ways such as general tidiness of its tips. This would improve its public image and make the MPAs more receptive when dealing with future spoil disposal applications. It would also be preferable to avoid adding another layer of bureaucracy onto the NCB which bringing spoil tips into the waste disposal licencing system would do.

Part 3
Conclusions & Recommendations

16.0 CONCLUSIONS ON THE EVALUATIVE FRAMEWORK

The Evaluative Framework has been designed to improve existing decision making processes with regard to the disposal of colliery spoil. It provides a more rigorous structure to the present informal process of evaluating between alternative sites. It has been tested against a variety of schemes selected as case studies.

The Framework has been shown to fulfil its four original objectives. It has proved to be comprehensive by testing it against a variety of disposal schemes, in different locations and using different handling and transport methods. It can also be used to test the best choice of originating colliery for a reception site, as well as the more normal approach of testing alternative disposal sites for a given colliery. In order to be this comprehensive, the Framework has to be relatively bulky, although it has been shown to be relatively quick to operate.

The Framework has also been demonstrated to have considerable flex-ibility provided that it is operated in a common-sense manner. It is perhaps most effective when different locations are involved and less sensitive to variations of a particular scheme in broadly the same location.

There were no problems of comprehension in terms of either the form or overall content of the Framework during the testing programme. It is likely that a co-ordinator would be required to translate all the varied inputs into the Fraemwork if it is to be completed in the most efficient manner. This role could be provided by NCB ORE or an outside consultant.

The Framework adopts a logical approach to building up information and justifying preferences between options. In certain sensitive circumstances it would be possible to restrict public access to detailed information in the Framework by the presentation of summary tables. This assumes, however, that MPA officers have been involved in the joint working during the course of running the Framework.

16.0 cont'd

The Evaluative Framework will hopefully encourage a more co-ordinated approach to the spoil disposal problem. It is likely to be used most effectively where there are established liaison arrangements between the NCB and MPA. Joint exercises to establish expected spoil arisings and the various time horizons when new tipping arrangements will be required, will often be a forerunner to the use of the Framework.

Used in this way the Framework should result in earlier agreement between the NCB and MPA and thus shorten the timescale for the granting of planning consent. In the event that agreement cannot be reached and a Public Inquiry results, the Framework should at least identify the areas of disagreement from those of agreed fact and provide a structured basis on which the investigations can take place.

Although the Evaluative Framework has been tested and refined against twelve case studies and has been used in part in the field, it is acknowledged that in each future application a close monitoring of its effectiveness will be needed. Indeed, in order to ensure its total application in the future it is essential that this monitoring exercise should be extensive and involve a continuing review and modification. A close analogy is COBA which is now in its ninth version.

17.0 CONCLUSIONS ON EXISTING SPOIL DISPOSAL PROCEDURES

This section identifies the main problems in existing spoil disposal practice and the key issues which need to be resolved if more innovative solutions are to stand a chance of being implemented. The Consultants have tried to be objective and offer comments on how existing procedures might be improved.

17.1 Spoil Production

The sheer scale of spoil productions and its increasing concentration in areas such as the Yorks, Notts, Derby coalfield is the starting point for this examination of the disposal problem. This concentration arises from the contraction of mining capacity in other UK coalfields, such as Scotland, the North East and South Wales. CENE quoted the Yorkshire and Humberside County Councils' Association's conclusion that, within the next 20 years, the same volume of spoil would need to be dumped in the Yorkshire area as over the whole of the previous 200 years. No subsequent information has come to light to alter this view. Within the central coalfield the search for tipping space is also becoming more localised because of the move towards concentration schemes with fewer but larger CPPs. There is also a trend towards a greater proportion of fines discard within spoil, which is a more difficult material to dispose of than coarse discard.

Spoil production will arise increasingly in new areas of the country not affected by a history of mining. This results from the need to open new fields to replace older fields now exhausted. The prospect of the development of a new coalfield in the Vale of Belvoir has already aroused great concern, not least because of the associated spoil disposal problems. Similar concerns will also no doubt be expressed with regard to the South Warwickshire coalfield. This was not the case with the development of Selby because run-of-mine was to be sent direct to nearby power stations with no creation of spoil.

17.1 cont'd

It does not appear to be a realist proposition to assume that significantly more colliery spoil can be sold commercially in the future even if NCB's Minestone Executive were able to improve its marketing procedures. There are many competing sources of waste material for use in the construction industry, and furnace bottom ash and pulverised fuel ash are likely to continue to be favoured over colliery spoil. Spoil has been successfully used as a bulk fill material for new roads built in coalfield areas but there is a limit to this outlet due to a reduced national motorway construction programme, irrespective of whether current dual tendering procedures are eventually improved.

Nor does it appear realistic to assume that CEGB will be willing to accept a higher dirt content in the fuel input to coal fired power stations (13-18% is the current range accepted). This would in any case merely pass on the problem. Indeed environmental pressures on the CEGB may force it to reduce the allowable dirt content even further. Underground stowage of colliery spoil may have potential but would involve high costs and technical difficulties.

The likelihood is, therefore, that the NCB will have to find disposal sites for around 50 million tonnes of spoil per year for many years to come. Some MPAs are concerned that the easy options for spoil disposal are fast being used up and that new sites will have to be found. This is in contrast to the CEGB's position of pfa disposal where existing sites, earmarked when power stations were built, are generally sufficient to cope with future output levels, bearing in mind the gradual run down of the coal fired stations and the better prospects for using pfa commercially. The severity of the spoil disposal problem is more akin to the difficulties many Waste Disposal Authorities are facing in finding suitable sites for solid waste. Indeed, in some areas, colliery spoil may be in direct competition for sites with solid waste, although in others there may be opportunities for co-disposal.

17.1 cont'd

A pre-requisite for tackling the spoil disposal problem on a comprehensive basis is to have some measure of likely spoil arisings
for each colliery in a given area. Because of inherent uncertain-
ties in mining conditions and the political difficulties of
revealing the implied lives of collieries, the NCB has been very
reluctant to produce any spoil forecasts. However, it is now
co-operating with the MPAs on joint exercises in both Yorkshire and
Nottinghamshire under the co-ordination of the DoE. Despite the
acknowledged difficulties it is hoped that meaningful estimates can
be offered to enable medium term planning to take place.

Future tipping capacity is generally planned for at NCB Area level
but on an individual colliery basis. The lack of a formalised
approach to forward programming of tipping capacity means that MPAs
may not be aware of the medium and long term need for tipping land
and it prevents consideration of, for instance, combined disposal
schemes for groups of nearby collieries. The latter is important,
when on an individual colliery basis, the economics prevent other
than the adoption of the cheapest solution. What is uneconomic for
a series of collieries individually may not be so when viewed
collectively.

In order to facilitate any forward planning of disposal problems
the NCB must make available its best assumptions about likely spoil
arisings. It is recognised that the NCB would not wish to
publicise detailed spoil production assumptions on an individual
colliery basis as this could carry obvious implications on
viability and life. However, even if global Area level estimates
were to be made available, this would assist other bodies, particularly the MPAs, to understand the anticipated scale of the
disposal problem and identify possible land for such use where an
environmental gain could be achieved.

17.0 cont'd

17.2 Organisational Procedures

The NCB has considerably improved its internal procedures regarding spoil disposal since the CENE report. It decided not to set up a specific department to be responsible for either spoil disposal or the environment, but instead to establish committees at HQ and Area level to take a co-ordinated view on environmental issues. In addition, all capital projects over £0.5 million, such as new mines, new CPPs and underground concentration schemes which are submitted for Board approval, have to demonstrate that adequate arrangements have been made for any associated spoil disposal requirements. All proposed spoil disposal schemes are also now subject to scrutiny by the NCB environmental checklist procedure.

The HQ Civil Engineering Branch acts in some senses as a national focus for spoil disposal and tries to disseminate best practice from particular Areas. Special seminars have also been organised on environmental issues to promote discussion between Areas.

Co-ordination has also been improved between Deep Mines and Open-cast and Minestone Executives over spoil disposal issues. Representatives of both Executives sit on the Area Surface Environment Committee and the Tips Sub-committee. Where it is possible to create a void by reshaping landforms, the Opencast Executive will accept spoil as a fill material subject to MPA approval. Such opportunities for dual use of land are unlikely to arise very often in the future as deep mines production in the central coalfield moves further east away from the exposed deposits. They are also unlikely to arise in the new greenfield locations, although opportunities for joint disposal with other surface mineral operators or with future coal based energy developments may arise.

17.2 cont'd

The extent to which NCB Areas involve MPAs in the forward choice of disposal sites varies according to the extent of informal liaison arrangements between the parties. In some Areas the arrangements appear to work well, in others there is room for improvement. Good working relationships are almost a pre-requisite to the effective use of the Evaluative Framework.

Apart from statutory consultations, informal liaison arrangments with third parties are handled on an ad-hoc basis. A possible model that might be considered for formalising relationships is the Working Party set up in Cornwall to deal with operational problems and forward planning in the china clay industry. This includes representation fro the operators (English Clays Lovering Pochin & Co. Limited), the MPA, District Councils, Highway Authorities and MAFF.

Another example involving CEGB are six monthly consultative committee meetings to consider the operational problems raised by the public at particular disposal sites. These committees usually consist of MPA and District Council representatives and Parish Councillors. The NCB rarely gets involved in public meetings exceptin advance of some controversial planning applications.

The sand and gravel industry has also taken part with local and central government in Regional Working Parties to discuss matching supply and demand in a way which minimises environmental disturbance. National guidelines have now been laid down (Circular 21/82) which, in areas of high demand such as the South East, commit operators to reducing the proportion of demand met by local resources over time for environmental reasons, with the balance to be made up by importing material (mainly crushed rock) from other regions. Section 8 grants for wagons and new rail head facilities are available but otherwise increased transport costs have to be reflected in the price to consumers. These voluntary arrangements are backed up by the powers of local authorities to refuse planning permission for the development of new gravel pits.

P

17.2 cont'd

Aggregate operators, by way of the Sand and Gravel Association, have also shown their concern for the environment by establishing their own system of restoration awards of best practice within the industry. They also operate a restoration fund to ensure adequate restoration of any site in the event of an operator going bankrupt.

It is fully appreciated that the circumstances of the aggregates industry, in terms of its ability to incur and pass on additional costs, are very different from those of the NCB.

The Consultants feel that informal arrangements offer scope for the Board to obtain environmental gain at very little cost. For example, many commentators have been critical of the environmental standards at GDO tips. Despite the fact that the Board does not see historical dereliction as its responsibility certain minor improvements associated with reclamation would cost relatively little compared to their benefits in public relations terms. It is understood that an initiative along these lines may be under consideration within the Board and is to be encouraged. The NCB might also consider introducing its own system of restoration awards either at Area or National level. The White Paper additionally refers to NCB's proposed competition "designed to encourage imaginative solutions to the spoil problem". However, since 1982 no announcement or details of this competition have been forthcoming.

Environmental expectations are rising in terms of the standards expected for spoil disposal schemes, as with all forms of land use. This influences the attitudes of communities traditionally dependent on coal mining as well as those in greenfield locations facing the prospect of mining for the first time. The NCB is conscious of the need to demonstrate its awareness of the environ-mental consequences of tipping and is investing in ways of ameliorating the adverse effects; for example visual screening and noise reduction. More could be done in this manner at some collieries.

17.2 cont'd

Legislative changes via the Minerals Act 1981 should assist MPAs in reviewing and updating planner permissions which inadequately safeguard environmental conditions. These are dependent on compensation scales still to be decided.

It does not appear appropriate to consider bringing NCB spoil disposal sites under Control of Pollution Act powers because of the degree of overlap with existing planning conditions and their ineffectiveness in dealing with restoration issues.

17.3 Disposal Methods

One of the most controversial issues raised during the Research Project has been the most appropriate disposal method for fines discard. It is fully appreciated that the material is a difficult substance to dispose of, whether by lagooning or dewatering equipment. The NCB is cautious of dewatering equipment because of its higher costs and manpower requirements, and questionnable reliability. The MPAs prefer dewatering equipment in environmental terms because of the greater chances of achieving progressive restoration when the material is handled dry. Their dislike of lagoons seems to reflect a criticism of the NCB's management of lagooning at some collieries, rather than the process itself. At other collieries early restoration of outer lagoon banks has been achieved.

While it would be wrong to suggest that lagooning is environmentally unacceptable in all locations (and pipelining as a means of transport causes virtually no nuisance), the Board will need to convince the MPAs that it will devote more attention to the management and phasing of lagoon facilities and particularly in their restoration. Each situation must, therefore, be taken on its merits and a trade-off made between additional costs of dewatering equipment and potential environmental gains. Although NCB has a rigorous research programme to test new forms of dewatering equipment it appears that once new equipment is installed at the collieries labour practices may impede the full realisation of cost savings.

17.3 cont'd

Another nationally controversial issue is the extent to which marine disposal methods are environmentally acceptable . This practice is restricted to the NCB North East Area and discharges both on the foreshore and at sea are strictly licensed. It was not part of this Project's remit to assess the consequences of these disposal practices. It appears from observation, however, that current output is being handled reasonably efficiently, bearing in mind the lack of alternative land-based sites available locally, but that more could be done to clean up the legacy left by unrestrained beach tipping.

The 1985 Coal Industry Act set NCB a two year target by which to break even and a target of 1990 by which to achieve a major degree of self financing. Understandably therefore it has to ensure that it is using cost effective disposal methods which, in most cases, means tipping as close to a colliery as possible providing that it is environmentally acceptable. (The difficulties of defining this latter term are fully accepted.) Historically, the NCB has selected its preferred scheme and submitted it in the form of a planning application to the MPA. If it were later found to be unacceptable or capable of modification the application would be withdrawn. The NCB is now more willing to look at options and to discuss them with the MPA before submission of an application. The use of the NCB's internal environmental checklist on its preferred option is designed to ensure that most issues are now resolved before the submission of an application.

Except in exceptional circumstances though, the NCB will rarely put forward a disposal scheme which involves the additional transport costs of going off-site where there are closer alternatives available. Although there are examples of spoil being disposed in mineral voids or opencast coal workings, these are relatively rare.

17.3 cont'd

In national environmental terms it is regrettable that farmland is being taken for tipping when unrestored voids are available elsewhere. The major constraint is the additional transport cost of remote disposal both in terms of start-up capital and annual operating costs although in the case of road transport there may also be environmental objections. Although it seems inequitable that some owners of voids try to levy tipping royalties for waste material which is being used to reclaim dereliction that they have themselves caused, this issue is small in relation to the burden of transport costs.

Although the NCB is prepared to adopt marginally increased costs on its least-cost scheme to obtain local environmental gain, understandably it will not willingly expend more money beyond this level. The chances of achieving wider use of voids for spoil disposal, therefore, rest on the extent to which some form of cost redistribution is possible, or an increase in the headroom of coal over other forms of energy.

17.4 Scope for Cost Redistribution

The NCB currently pays all the direct costs associated with spoil disposal. There are, however, a number of other parties, including local authorities, central government departments, transport operators, who might have an interest in encouraging more innovative spoil disposal solutions. Most schemes that have been proposed under this heading, such as the Pyewipe and Glews Hollow schemes, involve environmental advantages in terms of land reclamation in return for substantial additional costs compared with local tipping. Only the Welbeck scheme offsets additional spoil transport costs with cost savings; in this case on the solid waste disposal operation.

There are two instances where it might be feasible to think of other parties contributing to the costs of spoil disposal. One is where an environmentally acceptable local scheme had been suggested by NCB but a higher cost off-site solution was deemed to be preferable. The second would be as a means of encouraging higher environmental standards.

17.4 cont'd

However, there is no easily defined formula to produce cost-sharing acceptable to all participating parties. These parties will also, in practice, be subject to constraints on their own spending power.

However, if no subsidies are forthcoming and the "Polluter Pays Principle" is strictly enforced, it is unlikely that any remote spoil disposal schemes will be implemented. The MPAs are all too well aware that to reject a local tipping option in order to seek a remote alternative may prejudice the viability of a particular colliery and lead to threats of closure and consequent job losses.

Although there are no instances yet of other parties subsidising the NCB, various innovative schemes have been put forward as contenders for a share of the £2.5 million DoE fund set up by the White Paper, "Coal and the Environment". The first contribution went towards the costs of an experimental pipeline carrying spoil into the sea below the low water mark at Horden Colliery in the North East.

The second contribution has just been committed to the Welbeck scheme involving remodelling of existing landforms to reclaim existing dereliction caused by old colliery tips and sand and gravel workings. This scheme involves the co-disposal of colliery spoil and solid waste and takes advantage of the possibilities of savings on solid waste disposal and revenues from methane production cross-subsidising the additional transport costs involved in importing colliery spoil. Another contender for this money is a reclamation scheme at Goole (Glews Hollow) where an industrial after-use would produce revenues to offset the costs of the scheme. Derelict Land Grant money is also expected to make a contribution to both these schemes.

17.4 cont'd

Perhaps the greatest scope for using spoil to fill large scale voids, even if they are located remotely is from a new greenfield coalfield where the quantities and life of spoil production will be large and the capital cost of providing transport infrastructure will be a relatively small proportion of the total capital investment. Thus, it may be possible in these new situations to consider some form of remote disposal to extensive areas of voids which need to be filled such as the Bedfordshire brickfields. Indeed the Board may be forced to examine such options in the light of sustained objections to new tipping proposals.

There is an argument to suggest that central government should be prepared to assist with the organisation and costs involved in mounting schemes of this sort. As well as helping to reclaim extensive areas of dereliction which arose as a result of weaknesses in national planning legislation, the implementation of such schemes would lessen the pressure on the nation's land resources.

At a more local level the impetus for identifying off-site reclamation opportunities would more likely come from the MPA or groups of local authorities. In these circumstances one might expect them to take the lead in organising co-operative arrangements with the NCB and other parties. Bringing the various participants together in this way ought to ensure that their interests are properly represented, whilst at the same time providing a means of identifying and possibly resolving arrangements over costs. The local authorities would be in the best position to mobilise grant aid from appropriate sources, such as DLG and EEC funds, and should be prepared to make some contribution themselves.

Even when the DoE's present spoil demonstration fund becomes depleted, it may still be appropriate for them to make some financial contribution to semi-remote schemes which can be shown to be raising environmental standards and which are fostering a co-operative approach to tackling spoil disposal problems. This would require the DoE, at least temporarily, to extend their spoil disposal demonstration fund.

18.0 <u>RECOMMENDATIONS</u>

The main output of this Research Project has been the design and production of an Evaluative Framework. The first three recommendations are therefore:

1. NCB Areas and MPAs should together use the Evaluative Framework to assist decision making on colliery spoil disposal schemes.

2. In order that the Evaluative Framework is fully understood by these parties, particularly in areas of the country which have not been directly involved in this project, the DoE should organise a series of regional seminars. Issues to be discussed could include:
    - the purpose of the Evaluative Framework;
    - its derivation;
    - a practical demonstration of its use.

The Consultants would be pleased to assist in such seminars.

3. If found to be successful in practice, the Framework has the potential to be adapted for use in other parts of the minerals industry.

In addition to these three recommendations, the Consultants would like to put forward the following comments arising from their review of existing spoil disposal procedures. These comments are made to the Department of the Environment, as client, and are consistent with its overall responsibility for the national planning system.

The comments follow the order in which key issues were discussed in the preceding chapter. Recommendations 4, 7, 8, 12 and 15 are considered by the Consultants to be the most important practical measures to support the implementation of the Evaluative Framework which in turn should achieve improved procedures governing the disposal of colliery spoil.

18.0 cont'd

Spoil Production

4. NCB Areas should provide regular estimates of spoil production to the relevant Mineral Planning Authority to assist the forward programming of tipping capacity. An indication of land requirements should be capable of being incorporated into Structure and Local Plans where appropriate.

5. The pricing policy adopted by the Minestone Executive and the dual tendering system should encourage the maximum use of colliery spoil in reclamation work and for commercial uses. Negotiations should be carried out flexibly depending on the local circumstances.

Organisational Procedures

6. NCB Areas should continue to work closely with the Opencast Executive to identify opportunities for Deep Mines spoil disposal in opencast voids. Cross fertilisation of experience in restoration practice should also be encouraged.

7. NCB HQ should consider operating an award scheme to publicise best practice in spoil disposal between Areas. Such a scheme could be judged by an independent panel of experts in a similar way to the Business and Industry Panel for the Environment Awards.

8. NCB Areas and MPAs should consider adding to their existing liaison arrangements by the establishment of formal Working Parties at Area level. This would encourage greater co-ordination by allowing the different MPAs covered by an Area to be represented together with other interested parties such as MAFF and the Water Authority.

    This may be one way of safeguarding as far as possible the understanding which has been built up between local authority specialists and chief officers and NCB Areas, after the abolition of the Metropolitan County Councils.

18.0 cont'd

9.   NCB Areas should where possible discuss issues on a colliery basis with local community representatives. This should cover both day to day operational problems and forward planning of new facilities.

Disposal Methods

10. It is not possible to recommend a preferred method of disposal for colliery spoil. The most appropriate method will depend on local circumstances. The backfilling of voids and other poor quality areas would normally be favoured, where such options are practicable, over the use of productive farmland .

11. Where lagoons are currently in use or proposed for fines discard disposal, the NCB at colliery level should seek to improve its management control. In particular, attention should be paid to construction phasing, early overtipping and restoration with minimum time delay on completion of pumping. Where fines dewatering equipment has been installed at a colliery, the NCB should seek to use it to its maximum efficiency.

When planning new facilities for fines discard disposal the NCB should, with the use of the Evaluative Framework and in consultation with the MPA, assess between lagoons and dewatering equipment on the basis of relative costs and environmental consequences. The decision as to whether to proceed with a particular project remains with the NCB.

Scope for Cost Redistribution

12. The DoE should encourage the attainment of higher environmental standards by co-ordinating and disseminating information on innovative schemes and the use of planning conditions. It should continue to encourage the implementation of disposal schemes which make a significant contribution towards reclaiming dereliction and avoiding pressure on agricultural land, but where transport costs are acting as a constraint. The DoE should seek a budget so that it could contribute to the larger remote disposal schemes.

18.0 cont'd

13. Further investigation should take place on the application of the rating system to the NCB, the distribution of which takes no direct account of the environmental burdens on an area caused by spoil disposal. This situation also applies to other industries in respect of their waste disposal and it is recognised that this issue has wider implications beyond the Terms of Reference for this Project.

14. Owners of voids should not seek to levy tipping royalties for waste material which is being used to reclaim dereliction which they themselves have caused.

15. The DoE should consider extending its current spoil disposal demonstration fund to allow the realisation of semi-remote disposal schemes, where the environmental advantages justify it and where other parties are prepared to make some contribution towards the costs.

GLOSSARY

Aftercare — Maintenance of the tip after initial restoration to return the soil to good agricultural condition. Includes seeding, planting, cultivating, fertilising, watering and draining.

Aggregate — Broken stone, slag, gravel, sand or similar inert material which forms a substantial part of concretes, asphalts or roads.

Backstowing — The filling of an underground void from which mineral has been extracted by replacement with spoil or other material.

Capital Items — Items such as plant and machinery which are purchased for use over a number of years.

Capping (or Over-tipping) — Process of covering consolidated lagoon deposits generally with a layer of coarse discard.

CARBS — Computer program for visual assessment used by NCB's ORE on major projects (usually new mines).

Coal Preparation Plant — Process plant applying physical and mechanical processes to run-of-mine to make it suitable for particular uses.

Coarse Discard — Waste material from the coal washing process with a particle size greater than 0.5mm.

COBA — Cost benefit analysis computer program for evaluating economic benefits of highway schemes.

Colliery — A deep coal mining operation which incorporates the mine, coal preparation plant, engineering and materials supply installations along with facilities for mining operatives.

Compaction — The process by which the density of material is increased by rolling or by the passage of other mechanical plant to achieve closer packing of soil particles by explusion of air.

Consolidation — The time-dependent process by which soil particles are packed more closely together under the influence of loading through the expulsion of water.

GLOSSARY cont'd

Deep Mining

Mining in which access to the mineral deposits is obtained by means of shafts or drifts as opposed to excavation from the surface.

Depreciation

A proportion of the original cost of a capital item which is charged to the profit and loss account each year.

Dirt

General term for any extraneous material associated with the coal.

Discounted Cashflow

A technique for allowing different investment alternatives to be evaluated and compared. For a full discussion of discounted cashflow, see "Investment Appraisal in the Public Sector" H.M. Treasury, 1982.

Discount Rate

The rate used in a discounted cashflow calculation.

Drivage

The activity of cutting an underground roadway for access to coal face, transportation of run-of-mine and supplies, and for ventilation purposes.

Effluent

Waste water from a trade or process, or water from a surface or underground drainage operation which may be discharged to sewer or watercourse.

Equivalent Annual Cost

A technique which allows different cashflow profiles to be compared. It does so by reducing each to the Equivalent Annual Cost which would produce the same Net Present Value as the relevant cashflow.

Filter Cake

The partially dewatered product from the filtration process.

Filter Press

A batch process of pressure filter. Used for dewatering slurries containing fine solids (less than 0.5mm).

Filtration

A process for separating solids from liquids by allowing the liquid to pass through a finely woven cloth which retains the solids using vacuum or pressure to accelerate the separation.

Fines Discard

Waste material from the coal cleaning process with particle size less than 0.5mm.

GLOSSARY cont'd

Froth Flotation
A process for cleaning fine coal in which coal particles with the aid of reagents become attached to air bubbles in a liquid medium and float as a froth thus being separated from fine clays, etc., (known as tailings).

Gateside Pack
Tightly rammed material enclosed in walls of stone built on each side of a deep mine roadway to limit deterioration due to roof convergence following coal extraction.

Grading
The proportions of various grain sizes in a particulate material (well graded implies more or less uniform distribution from coarse to fine, poorly graded implies uniformity in size or lack of continuous distribution).

Greenfield Site
An area usually in agricultural or open use, which is proposed to be developed for mining or other industrial purposes.

Interest
Payments for the use of Loan Capital.

Lagoons
Settlement areas for material wholly or mainly in solution or suspension. Containments on tipping sites are generally constructed of coarse discard into which slurry or tailings in suspension are pumped to allow sedimentation of the solids and the discharge or re-use of the clarified supernatant water.

Leachate
Liquid that has percolated through soil or other medium and become polluted.

Life
The period of time over which a particular option is assessed.

Mineral Planning of Authority
Local Authority responsible for the control mineral workings under the Minerals Planning Act (usually the County Council).

Minestone
Unburnt colliery spoil, used for constructional purposes.

Moisture Content
Percentage by weight of total material.

MOSS
Computer program used in highway assessment studies.

GLOSSARY cont'd

Mulching	Laying of organic materials onto soil to improve its capacity to support vegetation by providing nutrients and improving soil structure, texture and moisture holding capacity.
Net Present Cost	The discounted value of a future stream of cash outflows. See also Net Present Value.
Net Present Value	The discounted value of a future stream of cashflows. For a fuller discussion, see "Investment Appraisal in the Public Sector", H.M. Treasury, 1982.
Opencast Mining	Mining of deposits in one or more seams by excavation from the surface after removal of the overlying deposits.
Operating Costs	Costs of materials and labour and other items used in the day to day operations.
Outturn Prices	Prices (and costs) expressed after taking account of assumed levels of inflation.
Overburden	Worthless rock or soil over the valuable mineral e.g. in an opencast mine.
Overheads	Costs which are not directly identifiable with any particular activity.
Poaching	Concentration of hoof marks and waterlogging on grazing land ususally at base of gradients
Raw Coal than	Coal which has received no preparation other possibly screening or crushing.
Real Prices	Prices (and costs) expressed in constant money terms without any allowance for inflation.
Reclamation	Combination of restoration and aftercare. In common usage the recovery of an area despoiled by industrial dereliction to beneficial use.
Restoration	After regarding of landform, sub-soiling, top-soiling and soil making process.
Ripping	Act of breaking to relieve compaction of soil forming materials (usually carried out by bulldozer - drawn heavy duty ripper or long angled steel tooth).
Run-of-mine	Raw mineral as raised from coal face prior to screening, crushing or preparation.

GLOSSARY cont'd

Run-off	Portion of rainfall that is not absorbed by deep strata, but is utilised by vegetation, lost by evaporation or finds it way into streams or surface flow.
Stripping	Process of removing soil forming materials in layers and respreading materials elsewhere (process usually carried out by motorised scrapers).
Screening	The separation of solid materials of different sizes by causing part to remain on a surface provided with apertures through which the remainder passes.
Seam	A stratum or layer or bed of coal or other mineral (generally applied to large deposits of coal).
Slurry	A suspension of fine raw coal with a particle size nominally less than 0.5mm in an aqueous medium.
Spoil	Waste (non coal) material extracted as a result of coal mining, variously known as dirt, waste, refuse, ash.
Spoil Heap	A tip of mining waste which is accumulated or deposited wholly or mainly in a solid state and not in solution or suspension.
Stacker Spreader	Device used in tipping of spoil which transfers and places spoil (also called radial spreader).
Stowage and Sub-soil	Space from which mineral has been extracted Weathered rock or soil lying immediately below top-soil (contains almost no organic matter).
Tailings	Reject from froth flotation process following the recovery of fine coal from slurries.
Thickening	The concentration of the solids in a suspension resulting in a product with a higher concentration of solids than in the original suspension. The process is often assisted by the use of flocculating agents.
Tining	Method by which top layers of restoration profiles are spiked to aerate soil, assist drainage and relieve compaction.
Tip	A spoil heap or lagoon.

GLOSSARY cont'd

Top-soil

Surface layer of soil rich in organic matter which provides physical support and nutrients to plants.

Visual Envelope

Map (VEM)

Area or land within which a spoil tip can be seen.

Void

Space behind advancing coal face left by mining of coal. Local terms are goaf or waste.

ABBREVIATIONS

BHRA	British Hydromechanics Research Association
BR	British Rail
CEGB	Central Electricity Generating Board
CENE	Commission on Energy and the Environment
COBA	Cost Benefit Analysis Program
COPA	Control of Pollution Act 1974
CPP	Coal Preparation Plant
cu.m	Cubic metres
DCF	Discounted Cash Flow
DDA	Deputy Director of Administration
DEF	Draft Evaluative Framework
DEn	Department of Energy
DLG	Derelict Land Grant
DoE	Department of the Environment
DTp	Department of Transport
EAC	Equivalent Annual Cost
EEC	European Economic Community
EF	Evaluative Framework
EFL	External Financing Limit
EIA	Environmental Impact Assessment
EPC	Environmental Planning Committee
GDO	General Development Order
Ha	Hectares
HGV	Heavy Goods Vehicles
HQ	Headquarters

IEA	International Energy Agency
IEF	Interim Evaluative Framework
IRR	Internal Rate of Return
LPA	Local Planning Authority
MAFF	Ministry of Agriculture, Fisheries and Food
ME	Minestone Executive
MMC	Monopolies and Mergers Commission
MPA	Mineral Planning Authority
NCB	National Coal Board
NCC	Nature Conservancy Council
NELP	North East Leicestershire Project
NFU	National Farmers' Union
NLF	National Loan Fund
NPC	Net Present Cost
NPV	Net Present Value
NSF	National Smokeless Fuels
OAP	Ove Arup & Partners
OE	Opencast Executive
ORE	Operational Research Executive
pfa	Pulverised Fuel Ash
PBSA	Planning Balance Sheet Analysis
PPP	Polluter Pays Principle
PSSSI	Possible Site of Special Scientific Interest
PV	Present Value

ABBREVIATIONS cont'd

RDWP	Remote Disposal Working Party
ROM	Run of Mine
RRR	Required Rate of Return
SSSI	Site of Special Scientific Interest
TRRL	Transport and Road Research Laboratory
VAT	Value Added Tax
VEM	Visual Envelope Map
WDA	Waste Disposal Authority
YAHCCA	Yorkshire and Humberside County Councils Association
Yorks,Notts,Derby Coalfield	Yorkshire, Nottinghamshire, Derbyshire Coalfield

REFERENCES

1. "Coal and the Environment"
   Commission on Energy and the Environment, (The Flowers Commission),
   1981

2. "Coal and the Environment"
   Government White Paper Cmnd 8877, May 1983

3. "Inspector's Report"
   The Vale of Belvoir Coalfield Inquiry, 1981

4. "Assessment of Major Industrial Applications : A Manual"
   PADC Research Team, Department of Geography, Aberdeen University
   Department of the Environment Research Report No.13, 1976

5. "Investment Appraisal in the Public Sector"
   H.M. Treasury, 1982

6. "North East Leicestershire Coalfield - Final Report"
   Remote Disposal Working Party, October 1983

7. "Comparative Costs of Different Methods of Dirt Disposal"
   National Coal Board Confidential Mining Committee Memorandum by
   Butler, M.H. & Dunn, R.B., July 1983

8. "Waste Disposal and the Environment"
   Blelloch, J.D., Colliery Guardian, p 392-401, August 1983

9. "North East Leicestershire Prospect - Final Report"
   Working Party on Underground Stowage, October 1983

10. "Use of Industrial By-products and Waste Materials in Building and
    Civil Engineering"
    BS 6543 - 1985 Section One

11. "Waste Disposal Statistics 1984-85 Estimates"
    CIPFA, 1985

12. "Proof of Evidence for North East Leicestershire Prospect Inquiry"
    Jenkinson, D.E. (NCB), 1979

13. "Additional Notes on the Treatment and Disposal of Fine Colliery
    Discards" for Ove Arup & Partners
    National Coal Board, 1985

14. "Tipping on Durham Beaches - Final Report"
    North East Working Parties on Colliery Waste, February 1980

15. "Conveying Limestone Aggregate and Colliery Spoil by Hydraulic
    Pipeline : Trials with a 156mm diameter pipe"
    TRRL Supplementary Report 354, 1978

16. "The Disposal of Solid Waste in Yorkshire and Humberside"
    Yorkshire and Humberside Regional Waste Disposal Working Group,
    March 1978

<u>REFERENCES</u> cont'd

17. "The Control of Mineral Working"
     Department of the Environment (Draft Revised Edition)

18. "The Establishment, Maintenance and Management of Vegetation on
     Colliery Spoil Sites"
     University of York Research Project, 1982

19. "The Use of Soils in Reclaiming Colliery Spoils"
     University of Newcastle Research Project, 1982

20. "Treatment of Deepmine Colliery Spoil"
     Forestry Commission Research and Development Paper 132, 1983

21. "Direct Free Seeding : A Potential Aid to Land Reclamation in
     Central Scotland"
     Arboricultural Journal, Volume 7, No.4, November 1983

22. "Dirt Disposal and the Environment"
     Abbot, J. and Bacon, A.R.,
     Symposium on Coal Preparation Plant Technology, p. 64-76,
     April 1983

23. Notes by Nottinghamshire County Council on Spoil Disposal Study and
     extracts from proceedings of North East Leicestershire Prospect
     (NELP) Inquiry on new coal mines in the Vale of Belvoir, 1985.
     (Letter 10th April 1985)

24. Joint Agricultural Land Restoration Experiments Progress Report
     No.2 - Bush Farm & Papercourt Farm
     DoE, MAFF, SAGA, 1982.

25. "National Coal Board"
     Monopolies and Mergers Commission Cmnd 8920, June 1983

26. "Colliery Spoil Study"
     Yorkshire and Humberside County Councils Association, June 1983

27. "Whither Derelict Land Grant"
     The Planner, January 1983

28. "Development Involving Agricultural Land"
     Department of the Environment Circular 75, 1976

29. "Reclamation at Pyewipe using Waste from the Yorkshire Coalfield -
     a Feasibility Study"
     Yorkshire and Humberside County Councils Association, January 1982

30. "Technical Memorandum No. H4/74 : The Use of Colliery Shale as
     Filling Material in Embankments"
     Department of Transport, April 1974

<u>REFERENCES</u> cont'd

31. "The Frost Susceptibility of Soils and Roads Materials"
     TRRL Report LR90, 1981

32. "Technical Memorandum (Bridges) BE 3/78 : Reinforced Earth
     Retaining Walls and Bridge Abutments for Embankments"
     Department of Transport, 1981

33. "An Investigation of Some Factors influencing the Suitability of
     Minestone as the Fill in Reinforced Earth Structures"
     National Coal Board Minestone Executive, 1983

34. "Cement Bound Minestone : User's Guide for Pavement Construction"
     National Coal Board Minestone Executive, 1983

35. "The Manufacture from Colliery Spoil of Synthetic Aggregate for use
     in Structural Concrete"
     Precast Concrete,
     March 1980, pp. 120-124 and April 1980, pp. 183-185

36. "An Assessment of Processes for the Manufacture of Synthetic
     Aggregates from Colliery Spoil"
     International Journal of Lightweight Concrete,
     September 1980, pp. 141-164

37. "The Manufacture of Synthetic Aggregates from Colliery Spoil"
     Building Research Establishment Information Paper IP 30/81,
     December 1981

38. "The Utilisation of Waste from Coal Mining in the United Kingdom"
     International Symposium, Turkey
     National Coal Board Minestone Executive, 1982

39. "1982 Annual Tip Review"
     National Coal Board, 1982

ASSESSMENT OF ALTERNATIVE COLLIERY SPOIL DISPOSAL OPTIONS

SPECIFICATION OF THE DEPARTMENT'S REQUIREMENTS

1. The Department of the Environment intends to fund research to expose the scale and distribution of costs and benefits arising from various spoil disposal options and to design a framework within which such options might be assessed. The completed framework would be used by the Department, local authorities and the National Coal Board to assess the options for future disposal schemes with a view to reaching agreement on cost-effective and environmentally acceptable methods of disposal.

OBJECTIVES

2. The objectives of this study are to:-

   i]   examine the current spoil disposal methods used in Britain for different types of spoil, including the management and financial aspects, based as far as possible on experience of a number of specific schemes;

   ii] examine and compare the costs and benefits arising from various spoil options applicable to particular situations, and design a framework which can be used to undertake a comparative assessment of the costs and benefits, including the environmental costs, of alternative disposal options as they might arise in relation to particular sites or areas;

   iii] identify particular problems as regards the distribution of costs amongst the different parties and suggest ways in which they might be resolved.

OUTLINE OF WORK

3. The project is expected to involve three main tasks:-

   A.   <u>A review of current spoil disposal methods for different types of spoil</u> 'run of mine, wet or washery dirt and tailings)

4. The review would concentrate on disposal methods used in Britain by the NCB, taking as a starting point how spoil, on reaching the surface, is generated and processed, and examining the nature and problems associated with different types of spoil. It would examine and report on the management and financial aspects associated with spoil disposal, including the various techniques for handling and transporting spoil and the methods used by the Board for landscaping and restoring disposal sites.

5. The review would also report on how the disposal of spoil is controlled and managed at individual colliery, NCB Area and national levels, including the role played by the Minestone Executive in promoting the utilisation of spoil.

6. Amongst the factors to consider in reviewing the different spoil disposal methods are:-

   a. how policies and statements in statutory plan documents affect the disposal of spoil;

   b. the interaction between planning requirements and the controls imposed on spoil disposal by other legislation (ie Mines and Quarries Tips Act 1969, Town and Country Planning (Minerals) Act 1981);

   c. the economic constraints, eg the requirement placed on the NCB to earn a satisfactory return on their assets, and in particular to minimise their operating costs;

   d. the technical constraints, eg the current limits to technology and prospects for the application of new techniques;

   e. the environmental constraints, eg the demands of other land uses including agriculture, and the visual impact of disposal sites;

   f. current practice in the disposal of other similar bulk wastes, eg pfa;

   g. how the General Development Order provisions as applied to many of the NCB tipping operations affect the disposal of spoil;

   h. other constraints, either real or perceived, which affect the disposal of spoil.

7. Although the review would concentrate on British spoil disposal practice the Department would welcome, for comparative purposes, an outline of overseas practice where relevant and within contractors' own experience, and in particular details of disposal methods (excluding underground stowage which is being examined elsewhere) not utilised in Britain.

B. The design and construction of a draft evaluative framework

8. An evaluative framework is required which would enable comparisons to be made between the costs and benefits arising from various spoil disposal options. The review would have identified the main factors which affect the management and financial aspects of spoil disposal, and these would serve as an important baseline from which the framework would be constructed. It is intended that the draft framework would be constructed and refined as far as practicable by an examination of the costs and benefits associated with specific schemes which are representative of a range of disposal options.

9. There are inevitably several different ways in which a framework to evaluate a range of disposal options can be constructed and the Department is prepared to consider alternative styles of presentation. However, it is anticipated that the framework would be so constructed that the costs and benefits associated with the following aspects can be determined for particular disposal schemes:-

   i. operational aspects: eg methods of coal-washing and handling, spoil transportation, restoration and aftercare;

9.   cont'd
   ii.   environmental aspects: eg land take, pollution, landscaping and aftercare;
  iii.   economic aspects: eg the scale and distribution of costs, the scale of disposal costs as a proportion of total coal production costs, loss of agricultural production, employment created, etc;
   iv.   management aspects: eg the planning, formulation and management of disposal schemes;
    v.   alternative uses: eg as a source of fill, or aggregate substitution.

C.   <u>Examination of disposal options</u>

10.   A number of disposal schemes, which are broadly representative of a range of disposal options, have been proposed for inclusion in the project by DOE on the basis of information provided by the NCB and lpa^s. The contractor would also be given the opportunity to suggest schemes with which he has been associated as further case studies.

11.   Using the draft evaluation framework designed and constructed at (B), each of the disposal schemes would be examined and assessed, identifying the costs and benefits associated with each scheme and a report prepared containing:

    i.   a detailed description of the scheme;
   ii.   a detailed account of the costs and benefits associated with the spoil disposal method(s) utilised for each scheme, indicating any factors which were not included in the draft evaluation framework or the review;
  iii.   details of any difficulties that were experienced in examining and assessing the scheme (ie because of an inadequate database).

12.   This detailed examination would lead to the refinement of the draft evaluative framework, and indicate particular areas of the assessment process where some redistribution of costs might produce a more efficient and equitable overall solution.

REQUIRED OUTPUT

13.   It is expected that the output from the research project as a whole would comprise:

a.   a draft interim report after 3 months containing -

    i.   a review of the management and financial aspects of current spoil disposal methods;
   ii.   a draft evaluative framework for examining the costs and benefits associated with various spoil disposal options;

13. cont'd

    b.   a draft <u>final report</u> after 12 months containing -

        i.   Report on each of the main disposal schemes included in the project;
       ii.   a synthesis of the main results of the examination and evaluation of the schemes;
     iii.   an appraisal of the effectiveness of the evaluation framework;
      iv.   a completed evaluative framework;
       v.   the identification of particular problem areas as regards the distribution of costs, and recommendations on how these might be resolved.

REPORTS

14. The reports would be typewritten and submitted to the Department in draft at dates to be agreed.

DURATION

15. Fifteen months.

PROJECT MANAGEMENT

16. Overall control of the project will rest with the Department's Nominated Officer who will be advised by a small Steering Group on which the NCB, local authorities and the Department of Energy will be represented along with DOE.

DOE will provide the chair and secretariat.

DOE

August 1983

NCB CHECKLIST FOR THE ENVIRONMENTAL ASSESSMENT OF MAJOR PROJECTS
[taken from Appendix I to CCI (83)33]

1. Is any part of the Project the subject of a formal planning applic-
    ation, or is it being submitted under the GDO?

2. Is there a presumption for or against the Project in the policies
    of the local authorities' Development Plans?

3. Is the Project dependent or likely to lead to a need for any
    further projects which could have adverse environmental impacts?

4. Have alternative schemes or sites been considered and if so is
    there any pressure from outside bodies to consider these further?

5. Are any environmental benefits obtained by carrying out this
    project?

6. In view of the answers to the questions above and the completed
    checklist overleaf, in the view of the Area, is the project or any
    aspects of it, likely to be taken to a Public Inquiry?

7. Has the full impact on the environment, both during the carrying
    out of the projects, and in the long-term afterwards, been
    considered?

R

Please complete the following:

(Notes on each heading are in Appendix II to this CCI)	Is this relevant?	Is there a problem? Who has been consulted, etc?	What assumptions costs have been included in the Scheme? Have alternatives been considered?

Visual

- visibility
- appearance in landscape

Noise

Dust & gaseous emissions

Water

- supply
- effluent and run-off

Land Use

- agriculture
- ecology
- recreation
- footpath diversions
- road closures
- archaeology
- minerals sterilisation

Traffic

- commuting
- HGV
- rail
- overland conveyors, etc.

Social

- employment
- infrastructure e.g. housing

Notes on each heading are in Appendix II to this CCI)	Is this relevant?	Is there a problem? Who has been consulted, etc?	What assumptions on costs have been included in the Scheme? Have alternatives been considered?

Effect on local economy

Subsidence

   housing
   services
   sensitive structures
   and
   drainage

Hazards to the public

Impacts arising after
the operation life of
the project

If the environmental issues for the construction phase are significantly different
or those for the operation phase, two checklists should be used for the two
phases.

Similarly if the project involves a significant solid waste disposal element,
an additional checklist (relating only to that) should be included.

NOTES OF GUIDANCE

Environmental Checklist

The checklist to be used is at Appendix I. It does not require that all potential problems have been resolved before the Stage II is submitted, so that submissions should not be delayed by this proposal.

The prime objective of the checklist is to identify any potential environmental problems and to assist the Board in the assessment of the project. Some entries on the checklist will be obvious and it may be possible to state with relatively little effort that some other types of problem will not occur. If the checklist identifies any potential problems - or if there are additional problems not identified on the list, further details of the issue, of any assessment work carried out and of the stage that consultations with local authorities, statutory bodies etc., have reached, should be given.

The following notes of guidance are presented in the form of a series of issues that might usefully be considered for each environmental impact, although other issues (not mentioned) may, of course, be relevant.

1. <u>Visual</u>

    (i)   Visibility

    Will the development be significantly overlooked? If so, from where - is it a sensitive location? Does the development break the skyline? If so, from where? What potential exists for screening the development?

    (ii)   Appearance in the landscape

    Will the development detrimentally alter the local landscape? Are landscaping measures needed to improve the visual impact of the development?

2. <u>Noise</u>

    Will the development significantly alter background noise levels during construction and operations? If so are complaints likely from local people? Will noise screening measures and/or sound insulation of buildings be necessary?

3. <u>Dust and Gaseous Emissions</u>

    Will there be any potential dust blow or gaseous emissions from the development and if so, what effect will it have on the locality? Will remedial measures be necessary and if so, what form will they take?

4. <u>Water</u>

    (i) Supply

    Does the development require a supply of water and how will it be obtained?

    (ii) Effluent and Run-off

    Will the development produce effluent and/or surface run-off and if so, do adequate disposal arrangements exist? Will effluents find their way into ground water and will this cause problems with water supplies? Are there local sites which are sensitive to the quality of water which will be affected?

5. <u>Land Use</u>

    (i) Agriculture

    Will agricultural land be taken and if so what MAFF Grade is it? Have you discussed this with MAFF, and what is their view? Will farm units be disrupted, severed or made unviable by the development?

    (ii) Ecology

    Will the development have any significant effect on sites of ecological value?

5.   cont'd

   (iii)   Recreation

Will the development have any significant effect on local amenity and recreational activities in the area?

   (iv)   Footpath Diversions

Do any footpaths cross the site and will they require diversion? What use is made of the paths? Has an alternative route been identified?

   (v)   Road Closures

Do any roads cross the site and will they require closure? What effect will closure have on the local community?

   (vi)   Archaeology

Will any site of archaeological interest be affected by the development?

   (vii) Minerals Sterilisation

Are any surface minerals present and will they be sterilised by the development? Is there any potential for prior extraction? What is the local authority Development Plan policy?

6.   Traffic

   (i)   Commuting

Will the development involve an increase in commuting traffic? If so, can the local road network cope?

   (ii)   HGV

Will the development involve an increase in HGV movements? If so, can the local road network cope? Are complaints likely from local residents due to noise, safety, etc?

   (iii) Rail

Will the development lead to increased rail movements? Will possible subsidence affect railway tracks?

   (iv)   Overland Conveyors, etc.

Will the development use overland conveyors, bucket carriers, etc., for the purpose of moving ROM or spoil?

7. Social

    (i) Employment

        Will the development have an effect on the local employment structures? If so, will it be beneficial or detrimental?

    (ii) Infrastructure

        Will the development entail the provision of further local infrastructure - e.g. houses, roads, sewage, services, schools, etc?

8. Effect on Local Economy

Will there be any effect on the local economy? If so, will it be beneficial or detrimental?

9. Subsidence

Will the development have any subsidence effects and if so will housing, services, sensitive structures and drainage be affected? What damage may result and what remedial measures may be necessary?

10. Hazards

Will there be any hazards to the public as a result of the development? Will they be temporary or permanent? What measures will be needed to safeguard the public?

11. Impacts after Operation Life

Are impacts likely after the operation life of the colliery? If so, what measures are necessary to ameliorate them?

COMPARISON OF EQUIVALENT ANNUAL COST
AND AVERAGE ANNUAL CASHFLOW MEASURE

Section 4.3 of the Report referred to the suggestion made by the NCB that the Equivalent Annual Cost (EAC) measure is needlessly complicated and that the average annual cashflow measure would be adequate in most cases. This Appendix shows a hypothetical example to illustrate the scale of difference that could arise between the two measures.

Consider a hypothetical example where most of the cost of a scheme is taken up in land acquisition and capital works. Actual operating costs are low. The cost structure is:

Year	Capital £'000	Operating £'000	Total £'000	Tonnes Tipped >000
1	1000		1000	
2	1000		1000	
3		300	300	500
4		300	300	500
5		300	300	500
6		300	300	500
7		300	300	500
			3500	2500

Total cash outflow is £3,500,000 and 2,500,000 tonnes are tipped. The average cash costs per tonne are therefore £1.40.

The EAC, however, is £1.55, a difference of 10%.

WEIGHTING/SCORING SYSTEM

This appendix records the final form of the Weighting/Scoring system which represents the third of the decision aiding tools in Phase III of the Draft and Interim Evaluative Frameworks. The reasons for its exclusion from the final Framework are given in Section 4.5.

1.   Statement on Weighting

    Give reasons for the distribution of weights between broad economic and environmental groupings, then the sub-division to individual factors.

2.   Statement on Scoring

    Give reasons for the allocation of scores between options on each economic and environmental factor highlighting relative performance.

PHASE III

WEIGHTING/SCORING SYSTEM

	Weights	Option A		Option B		etc.
		Score	Weight x Score	Score	Weight x Score	

ECONOMIC

EAC/Tonne or /m³

Initial Cost

ENVIRONMENTAL

Visual	– Operational
	– Final Form
Land Use	– Operational
	– After-use

Ecological and Heritage

Recreational

Pollutants	– Water
	– Air
	– Noise

Transport Route

Other Factors

TOTAL   100

% of Points Total

1. Distribute 50 weights between the economic factors (applicable to all columns).
    Distribute 50 weights between the relevant environmental factors (applicable for all
    columns). Highest values reflect those factors of greatest importance.

2. Distribute scores across each row, giving 10 to best option, 1 to worst option and scoring
    the remainder within this range according to relative performance.

3. Environmental entries are only made where impacts are significantly different between
    options and judged to be critical to the decision between these options.

4. For each option multiply score by weight, sum down each option column.

5. High option totals imply preferred options.

6. Calculate the percentage distribution of points between options. This allows comparison
    between projects where different numbers of weights and scores have been assigned.

7. Repeat the method using different weight systems to show sensitivity of results or
    construct diagram.

PHASE III

Sensitivity Test on Weighting/Scoring System

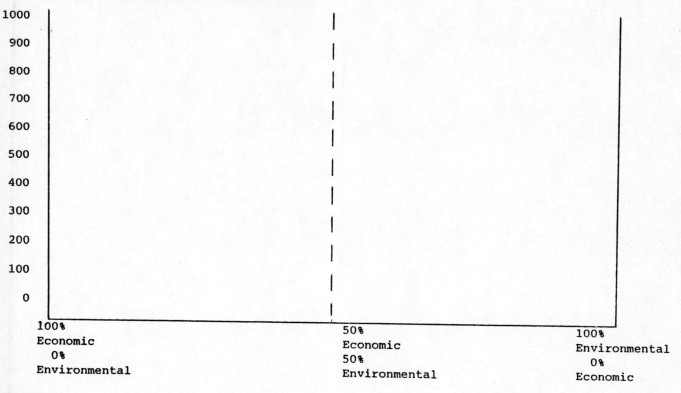

METHOD

1.   Sum the points total for each option on economic factors and double them.
      Plot relative positions on the left hand vertical axis. This is equivalent to attaching
      100% of the weights to economic factors.

2.   Repeat for environmental factors and plot on right hand vertical axis.

3.   Construction option lines by joining left and right axes. Check that relative position of
      options along a mid point vertical line (50/50 weightings) corresponds with that
      calculated in the Weighting/Scoring table.

4.   Option preferences for any combination of weightings can then be deduced for given
      scorings.

5.   Preferred options on any given weighting system is shown by the uppermost line on the
      graph. If different scorings are used different graphs will result.

UTILISATION OF SPOIL

Introduction

Table 6.3 of the report outlined the main commercial uses to which spoil
is put together with their relative importance. This Appendix describes
these uses in more detail and comments on their potential for future
growth.

The Minestone Executive of the NCB is responsible for the utilisation of
unburnt spoil (or minestone) which is not tipped. Currently it is
spending £0.25m per annum on research to upgrade the acceptability of
spoil in various commercial uses.

In dealing with the current types of utilisation, there are three major
uses.

Use as Bulk Fill

The most significant use of spoil (77% of the total in 1976) is for bulk
fill material in civil engineering works; mainly road construction.
Recent landfill and reclamation sites, dams, rivers, canals, reservoirs
and flood protection work bunds have also made use of colliery spoil in
this way.

Historically, shales burned in uncompacted tips and the resulting material compared favourably with naturally occurring rock and engineering
soils used as common fill for infilling low-lying ground and for the
construction of road and rail embankments. In the early 1960's the
Ministry of Transport specifications restricted such uses to burnt
shales only as unburnt shales were considered to be susceptible to
spontaneous combustion. But in 1968 the Ministry allowed the use of
unburnt shale on an experimental basis. Minestone was used in trunk
roads and motorway projects close to coalfields as a trial and was

eventually accepted as a fill material by the Department of Transport in 1974 (Ref. 30). In the meantime, stocks of well burnt shales in tips were depleted and the amount of minestone remained abundant (3000 million tonnes in October 1982). Nevertheless, it has been used extensively for motorway embankments in the road building programme, for railway embankments as in Croydon and at Pegwell Bay International Hoverport, Ramsgate.

A particular use is the construction of minestone bunds to form lagoons for settling of pulverised fuel ash (pfa) from coal fired electricity generating stations as illustrated by the Gale Common Scheme. Further examples of bulk fill are filling of disused quarries, gravel and clay pits and sealing off and protection cover for solid waste landfill sites.

Though the characteristics of minestone varies from source to source and sometimes between parts of a spoil heap, it has three general features which facilitate its use as bulk fill. These are:-

    i]   its ease of compaction into stable fill of high dry density;

    ii]   its tendency, on the basis of TRRL Report LR90 test (Ref. 31), not to be frost susceptible. It can hence be used within 450mm of the surface in highway and related constructions - for example, car parks and hardstandings - without risk of frost induced failure;

    iii] its low levels of highly soluble sulphates - high levels of sulphates in ground containing moving ground water can cause damage to adjacent concrete structures.

The range of applications as bulk fill can be extended by mechanical ground treatment techniques such as dynamic compaction, vibro-floatation and the use of a layer of a separation membrane.

Use in Retained Earth Structures

Reinforced earth is a composite building material formed by the inter-action of tensile reinforcing members and soil. Reinforced earth is used for retaining walls and bridge abutments. Burnt shale has been used successfully for this purpose both within the NCB and by the Department of Transport. The Minestone Executive, in collaboration with the Coal Research Establishment, the Scientific Department of the NCB, and various universities is currently investigating the utilisation and exploitation of minestone (unburnt shale) as an additional acceptable material for use in reinforced earth.

Though reinforced minestone has been used successfully in retaining walls at NCB sites (six such schemes have been completed), the Department of Transport only recognises the use of burnt spoil as suit-able for this purpose. Minestone is specifically classified as unsuitable fill for structures covered in Technical Memorandum BE 3/78 (Ref. 32). The Memorandum identifies minestone as a potential drainage and durability hazard. Nevertheless, the Executive is seeking the material's acceptance. A programme of investigation has thus been initiated by the Executive to demonstrate the suitability of minestone in reinforced earth structures. The areas which are being studied in particular are its heat gain, potential acidity, swelling and wet weather construction.

An interim report on reinforced minestone was published by the Minestone Executive in August 1983 (Ref. 33). Further papers have also been published in various journals, which underlines the Executive's keenness to promote the use of reinforced earth.

Use as Cement Stabilised Sub-base
for Roads and Hard Surfaces

When Ordinary Portland Cement is added to minestone it acts as a stabil-iser and improves the material's strength and other physical properties.

This enables the minestone to be used in more structurally demanding applications. The Minestone Executive has produced a Users Guide for Cement Bound Minestone (Ref. 34) which gives a full description of the method of manufacture and associated tests of its properties. Examples of applications include roads, airfields, hard shoulders, site roads, footpaths, factory floors, vehicle parking areas, hardstandings, material stocking areas, oversite and blinding 'concrete' and, more recently, as an underlay for block paving.

The use of cement stabilised minestone has only developed in the last seven years and hence is not quantified in Table 6.3 of the report. However, significant amounts of spoil have been used for this purpose. For example, spoil from Kent collieries was used to form the top surface of the apron areas at Ramsgate Harbour and it was also used at Sheerness.

In addition to the above three major uses there are two other areas of current use; unburnt spoil being used as a raw material in cement manufacture and brick making.

Turning to the future possibilities for use of spoil, there are two major areas of interest.

Use as Aggregate for Lightweight Blocks

In 1976, the Department of Environment's Building Research Establishment started a research programme to investigate the possibility of producing a synthetic aggregate from colliery spoil. The laboratory investigation of the method and recommendations on possible routes to manufacture the aggregate, together with an assessment of the economics of the process are described in two papers (Refs.35,36). The papers identified two radical developments which would be required in order to make the manufacture of synthetic aggregates from colliery spoil more economically competitive:-

a] design of lightweight kilns and heat exchangers which dispense with heavy, bulky refractories by using high temperature alloys, hence reducing capital costs;

b] use of mineral processing techniques to produce a fraction rich in combustibles which could be used as a fuel and a fraction very low in combustibles which could be used as a raw material for aggregate manufacture.

The Building Research Establishment, which has not carried out further experimental work since the publication of an Information Paper on this subject in December 1981 (Ref. 37), regards the capital cost of equipment as the major disadvantage. Although successful in utilising minstone an early scheme at Snowdon Colliery, Kent ran into problems of air pollution.

There is currently only one interest in the use of spoil for lightweight aggregate. In June 1982, Thermal Conversions (UK) Limited was established as a company to further the development of a new rotary kiln. The kiln is about 16m long with an outer diameter of 3m. It is lined with an aircraft-grade nickel alloy steel shaped into a trefoil cross section. The lining is backed by a ceramic insulation all inside a mild-steel shell. The kiln weighs about 30 tonnes which is less than one third of the weight of a conventional kiln.

A pilot plant was built in 1982 at Longfield, Kent which demonstrated the high thermal efficiency of the process. This resulted in Thermal Conversions being awarded a Department of Industry grant towards the capital costs of a full scale demonstration plant, under the Energy Conservation Demonstration Projects Scheme. The grant is being admin- istered by the Energy Technology Support Unit. Financial backing is also being provided by Flextech plc, the British Technology Group and Electra Risk Capital. Other bodies which have provided assistance are British Ceramic Research and the Cement & Concrete Association.

Tests were initiated at several collieries to determine the suitability of the material for conversion into aggregate and Abernant Colliery in South Wales was selected as the site for Thermal Conversions' first full-scale demonstration plant. The initial plant was commissioned in November 1985 and the technical capability has been established. The second phase of the project, to bring it to a commercial scale of production, is now under way. It has been established that a larger volume, lighter product can be produced.

The process at Abernant Colliery is as follows:-

a]   Spoil (initially only tailings from deep cones thickeners) is transported from the tip at Abernant Colliery by tanker lorry over a distance of about 500m and discharged to a holding tank.

b]   The tailings mix is then air entrained, extruded and dried, before screening to a size range of 3-10mm.

c]   The pellets are then fired at 1000°C in the rotary kiln for about 2 hours at a speed of 2 to 3 revolutions per minute. The burning of the carbon content of the tailings is used to fuel the kiln. The kiln operates in combination with a product cooler which provides pre- heated air for the combustion of fuel in the kiln. This results in considerable energy saving by reclaiming heat from the hot product.

d]   The synthetic aggregate product is collected by lorries and trans- ported to concrete manufacturers. There are several local concrete blockmakers near the colliery and it is hoped that the initial level of output will be sufficient to supply all of them with their total requirement of aggregate.

The washery at Abernant Colliery produces about 45,000 tonnes of very fine tailings a year. Disposal problems caused by a shortage of land for lagoons and inappropriate terrain for local tipping require existing tailings to be stabilised with cement before tipping. As this is expensive, the colliery was keen to encourage alternative methods of disposal.

Other attractions of the Abernant Colliery which results in its selection for Thermal Conversions' first test plant are:-

a] The froth flotation cells are operated very efficiently giving a fairly consistent grained product with a low free coal content;

b] The colliery is expected to have a long life;

c] The coal is anthracitic and hence low in sulphur and volatiles;

d] The colliery site has space for a tailings treatment/lightweight aggregate plant.

Though the volume of crushed shale is much higher than the volume of tailings, the NCB is keen to solve the tailings disposal problem first. The plant will convert only the tailings (25,000 dry tonnes/annum) to lightweight aggregate, no crushed coarse discard being required.

The kiln is anticipated to operate 24 hours a day and 5 days a week. The firing temperature can be increased according to the strength of concrete aggregate desired. Aggregate size can also be manufactured to requirement by controlling screen size.

Lightweight aggregate concrete has been extensively used for many years in North America, but less so in the rest of the world. Its technical viability and other advantages such as reduction in use of resources, reduced energy demand and quicker production potential have long been recognised by structural engineers. However, its application to the structural field is far from extensive and this is due to one of its few disadvantages, namely the high price of manufacture of lightweight aggregates, which costs up to twice that of gravel or marine aggregates.

From laboratory tests on the new kiln, it has been shown that its low capital cost of plant, together with the high thermal efficiency of the process, which produces a good standard of aggregate, is a promising innovative scheme for the use of colliery spoil by this means.

Use in Hydroponics, Horticulture and Agriculture

Hydroponics is defined as the soil-less cultivation of plants which receive nutrition directly from water. When minestone is placed in a fluidised bed combuster, fluidised bed ash pellets are produced and these can provide mechanical support to the plant and its roots. However, careful control must be exercised to ensure the minestone does not contain toxic metals harmful to the plant (Ref.38).

Other applications in agriculture and horticulture which the Minestone Executive has investigated in conjunction with the MAFF, include 'crocking', 'benching', ring culture, land drainage and soil improvement. The use of spoil in this field, however, is on a very small scale.

CURRENT DISPOSAL METHODS IN THE

YORKS, NOTTS, DERBY COALFIELD

Introduction

Section 7.1 of the report outlines methods used for colliery spoil disposal and their relative importance nationally. This Appendix describes in more detail the methods currently used in the Yorks, Notts, Derby coalfield.

Local tipping is the dominant form of spoil disposal in the central coalfield area and concern at the increasing amount of land that would be required here for this purpose, if present trends continue, was one of the main reasons for the establishment of this current study.

The number of active spoil tips currently within the coalfield is 174, together with 70 closed and 26 disused tips. The number of active collieries is about 100. The number of tips in each of the seven pre-1985 NCB Areas in the coalfield is shown on Table F1.

TABLE F1

NUMBER OF TIPS BY NCB AREA

	Active Tips	Closed Tips	Disused Tips
Y/N/D Coalfield			
North Yorkshire	39	9	2
Doncaster	11	12	-
Barnsley	23	20	6
South Yorkshire	30	9	7
North Nottinghamshire	30	8	-
South Nottinghamshire	19	1	3
North Derbyshire	22	11	8

Source : NCB 1982 Annual Tip Review (Ref. 39)

The total volume of tips in the coalfield is estimated by the NCB at about 515 million cubic metres covering an area of some 4,500 hectares. The maximum volume of spoil which could be tipped within the extent of current planning permissions is estimated by the NCB to be just over 835 million cubic metres occupying a total tipping area of some 5,900 hectares. The breakdown of these figures by NCB Area is shown in Table F2.

TABLE F2

VOLUME AND AREA OF EXISTING AND PERMITTED
TIPS BY NCB AREA

	Total Volume of Existing Tips ('000 cu.m)	Existing Area Covered by Spoil (Ha)	Design Capacity of Permitted Tips ('000 cu.m)	Total Permitted Tipping Area (Ha)
Y/N/D Coalfield				
North Yorkshire	50,950	602.1	68,216	648.6
Doncaster	69,690	517.0	94,963	647.0
Barnsley	74,158	546.2	94,856	613.9
South Yorkshire	86,973	760.7	161,801	1,009.4
North Nottinghamshire	94,385	793.8	191,333	1,311.3
South Nottinghamshire	74,146	678.4	125,660	825.3
North Derbyshire	64,984	592.5	100,294	855.2

Source : NCB Questionnaire Response

Tipping is becoming increasingly concentrated at a number of large complexes. This is often done by linking collieries underground and bringing the run-of-mine to the surface at one central location. Surface means of transport may also be used to collect run-of-mine from other collieries for processing at a central CPP. This process of concentration is most advanced in the former NCB Barnsley Area where production is now centred on three main complexes: Grimethorpe, South Kirkby and Woolley.

Handling and transport of spoil in the Yorks/Notts/Derby coalfield area is predominantly undertaken by mobile earth moving equipment for solids and pipelining to lagoons for wet discard. The exceptions are:-

- an aerial ropeway at Kiveton Park Colliery in South Yorkshire Area, although this was due to be replaced by a conveyor and bulldozer system late in 1984;

- the new stacker spreader at Grimethorpe Colliery, with a second installation on the new South Kirkby tip, both in Barnsley Area;

- side tipping rail wagons in association with scrapers or dump trucks at Allerton Bywater and Wheldale in North Yorkshire Area and Moorgreen in South Nottinghamshire Area.

The NCB has won planning permissions for additional local tipping capacity at most of its long life collieries in the coalfield. There is widespread feeling amongst the planning authorities, however, that the easy options for local tipping are running out and that attention should now be given to looking for more environmentally acceptable alternatives before new capacity is required.

There is currently little transport of spoil to surface voids or land-fill schemes in the central coalfield. Details of those schemes that are in operation, together with the method of transport and type of disposal site are shown in Table F3. Distances involved are relatively short, mostly less than 2-3 kilometres, often using private haul roads or pipelines across NCB land.

TABLE F3

SPOIL DISPOSAL SCHEMES INTO SURFACE VOIDS IN YORKS, NOTTS, DERBY COALFIELD

AREA	COLLIERY	TYPE OF DISCARD	DISPOSAL POINT	METHOD OF TRANSPORT	HAUL DISTANCE MILES	AMOUNT (TONNES/ANNUM)
North Yorkshire	Ackton Hall	Coarse	Springfield Opencast Site	Private Road	0.5	420,000
	Prince of Wales	Coarse	Cornwall Opencast Site	Private Road	0.5	319,000
	Sharlston	Coarse	Snydale Opencast Site	Private Road	1.0	450,000
	Kellingley	Pressed Tailings	Private quarry	Public Road	3.0	90,000
	Kellingley	Coarse	Gale Common (joint CEGB/NCB disposal)	Public Road	1.5	800,000
South Yorkshire	Brookhouse	Coarse	Opencast Site	Private Road	0.5	325,500
	Thurcroft	Tailings	Board owned clay quarry	Pipeline	0.5	24,500 (solids)
South Nottinghamshire	Gedling	Tailings	Sand and gravel workings	Pipeline	2.5	1,000 (estimated)
	Bentinck	Coarse	Bentinck Opencast site	Conveyor	0.5	1,200,000
North Derbyshire	Markham/Ireland (from Sept. '84)	Coarse	Erin Opencast site	Private Road	1.0	1,200,000 (estimated)

Source : NCB Questionnaire Response

The transport infrastructure of the Yorks, Notts, Derby coalfield area lends itself to the consideration of alternative forms of spoil disposal. Besides road access to all collieries, many are directly linked to the rail network; indeed a lot of coal is taken by rail, typically using merry-go-round trains to the major power stations. In addition, the coalfield area contains most of the commercial waterways in the UK. The NCB already has six wharves on the Aire and Calder Navigation (although some of these are at collieries which have now closed) and about 2 million tonnes of coal were transported to market by barge in this area in 1980.

ACKNOWLEDGEMENTS

The Consultants' Study Team would like to thank the many individuals who have readily given time and information to assist the Team in carrying out this Research Project. The individuals are too numerous to mention but represented the following bodies:-

Central Government

        Department of Energy - Coal Division
        Department of Energy - Energy Technology Division
        Department of the Environment - Minerals Planning Division and
                                      Regional Offices
        Ministry of Agriculture, Fisheries and Food

National Coal Board

        Barnsley Area
        Construction and Civil Engineering Branch
        Doncaster Area
        Finance Department
        Headquarters Liaison Group
        Markham Main Colliery
        Minestone Executive
        North Derbyshire Area
        North East Area
        North Nottinghamshire Area
        North Yorkshire Area
        Opencast Executive
        Operational Research Executive
        Penalta Colliery
        Regional Scientific Office - Yorkshire
        South Nottinghamshire Area
        South Wales Area
        South Yorkshire Area
        Surveyors Department

Local Authority Planning Departments

        Barnsley District Council
        Boothferry District Council
        Cornwall County Council
        Durham County Council
        Derbyshire County Council
        Easington District Council
        Humberside County Council
        Mid Glamorgan County Council
        North Yorkshire County Council
        Nottinghamshire County Council
        Selby District Council
        South Yorkshire County Council
        Tyne and Wear County Council
        Wakefield District Council
        West Yorkshire County Council

ACKNOWLEDGEMENTS cont'd

Other Bodies

British Rail Freight Directorate
Central Electricity Generating Board
English Clays Lovering Pochin & Co. Limited
National Farmers Union
Severn Trent Water Authority
Standard Railway Wagon Co. Limited
Thermal Conversions (UK) Limited

STUDY TEAM MEMBERS

Malcolm Simpson	Ove Arup & Partners	Director in Charge
Malcolm Noyce	Ove Arup & Partners	Project Leader
Malcolm Fullard	Ove Arup & Partners	
Anil Iyer	Ove Arup & Partners	
John Shaw	Ove Arup & Partners	
Sarah Turner	Ove Arup & Partners	
Mark Bostock	Arup Economic Consultants	
Terry Hill	Arup Economic Consultants	
Corinne Swain	The Economic & Transport Planning Group	Deputy Project Leader
David Broadbent	Consultant	
Douglas Sampson	Derek Lovejoy & Partners	
Martin Kelly	Derek Lovejoy & Partners	
Julian Bagwell	Touche Ross & Co.	

Printed in the United Kingdom by Her Majesty's Stationery Office, Edinburgh Press
Dd 290878 C8 6/88 (257544)